INTERMEDIATE 2

CHEMISTRY
2009-2013

HODDER
GIBSON
LEARN MORE

Hodder Gibson is grateful to the copyright holders, as credited on the final page of the Question Section, for permission to use their material. Every effort has been made to trace the copyright holders and to obtain their permission for the use of copyright material. Hodder Gibson will be happy to receive information allowing us to rectify any error or omission in future editions.

Hachette UK's policy is to use papers that are natural, renewable and recyclable products and made from wood grown in sustainable forests. The logging and manufacturing processes are expected to conform to the environmental regulations of the country of origin.

Orders: please contact Bookpoint Ltd, 130 Park Drive, Abingdon, Oxon OX14 4SE. Telephone: (44) 01235 827720. Fax: (44) 01235 400454.

Lines are open 9.00–5.00, Monday to Saturday, with a 24-hour message answering service. Visit our website at www.hoddereducation.co.uk. Hodder Gibson can be contacted direct on: Tel: 0141 848 1609; Fax: 0141 889 6315; email: hoddergibson@hodder.co.uk

This collection first published in 2013 by

Hodder Gibson, an imprint of Hodder Education,

An Hachette UK Company

2a Christie Street

Paisley PA1 1NB

{BrightRED Hodder Gibson is grateful to Bright Red Publishing Ltd for collaborative work in preparation of this book and all PUBLISHING SQA Past Paper and National 5 Model Paper titles 2013.

Typeset by PDQ Digital Media Solutions Ltd, Bungay, Suffolk NR35 1BY

Printed in the UK

A catalogue record for this title is available from the British Library

ISBN 978-1-4718-0245-4

3 2 1

2014 2013

Introduction

Study Skills – what you need to know to pass exams!

Pause for thought

Many students might skip quickly through a page like this. After all, we all know how to revise. Do you really though?

Think about this:

"IF YOU ALWAYS DO WHAT YOU ALWAYS DO, YOU WILL ALWAYS GET WHAT YOU HAVE ALWAYS GOT."

Do you like the grades you get? Do you want to do better? If you get full marks in your assessment, then that's great! Change nothing! This section is just to help you get that little bit better than you already are.

There are two main parts to the advice on offer here. The first part highlights fairly obvious things but which are also very important. The second part makes suggestions about revision that you might not have thought about but which WILL help you.

Part 1

DOH! It's so obvious but …

Start revising in good time

Don't leave it until the last minute – this will make you panic.

Make a revision timetable that sets out work time AND play time.

Sleep and eat!

Obvious really, and very helpful. Avoid arguments or stressful things too – even games that wind you up. You need to be fit, awake and focused!

Know your place!

Make sure you know exactly **WHEN and WHERE** your exams are.

Know your enemy!

Make sure you know what to expect in the exam.

How is the paper structured?

How much time is there for each question?

What types of question are involved?

Which topics seem to come up time and time again?

Which topics are your strongest and which are your weakest?

Are all topics compulsory or are there choices?

Learn by DOING!

There is no substitute for past papers and practice papers – they are simply essential! Tackling this collection of papers and answers is exactly the right thing to be doing as your exams approach.

Part 2

People learn in different ways. Some like low light, some bright. Some like early morning, some like evening / night. Some prefer warm, some prefer cold. But everyone uses their BRAIN and the brain works when it is active. Passive learning – sitting gazing at notes – is the most INEFFICIENT way to learn anything. Below you will find tips and ideas for making your revision more effective and maybe even more enjoyable. What follows gets your brain active, and active learning works!

Activity 1 – Stop and review

Step 1

When you have done no more than 5 minutes of revision reading STOP!

Step 2

Write a heading in your own words which sums up the topic you have been revising.

Step 3

Write a summary of what you have revised in no more than two sentences. Don't fool yourself by saying, 'I know it but I cannot put it into words'. That just means you don't know it well enough. If you cannot write your summary, revise that section again, knowing that you must write a summary at the end of it. Many of you will have notebooks full of blue/black ink writing. Many of the pages will not be especially attractive or memorable so try to liven them up a bit with colour as you are reviewing and rewriting. **This is a great memory aid, and memory is the most important thing.**

Activity 2 — Use technology!

Why should everything be written down? Have you thought about 'mental' maps, diagrams, cartoons and colour to help you learn? And rather than write down notes, why not record your revision material?

What about having a text message revision session with friends? Keep in touch with them to find out how and what they are revising and share ideas and questions.

Why not make a video diary where you tell the camera what you are doing, what you think you have learned and what you still have to do? No one has to see or hear it but the process of having to organise your thoughts in a formal way to explain something is a very important learning practice.

Be sure to make use of electronic files. You could begin to summarise your class notes. Your typing might be slow but it will get faster and the typed notes will be easier to read than the scribbles in your class notes. Try to add different fonts and colours to make your work stand out. You can easily Google relevant pictures, cartoons and diagrams which you can copy and paste to make your work more attractive and **MEMORABLE**.

Activity 3 – This is it. Do this and you will know lots!

Step 1

In this task you must be very honest with yourself! Find the SQA syllabus for your subject (www.sqa.org.uk). Look at how it is broken down into main topics called MANDATORY knowledge. That means stuff you MUST know.

Step 2

BEFORE you do ANY revision on this topic, write a list of everything that you already know about the subject. It might be quite a long list but you only need to write it once. It shows you all the information that is already in your long-term memory so you know what parts you do not need to revise!

Step 3

Pick a chapter or section from your book or revision notes. Choose a fairly large section or a whole chapter to get the most out of this activity.

With a buddy, use Skype, Facetime, Twitter or any other communication you have, to play the game "If this is the answer, what is the question?". For example, if you are revising Geography and the answer you provide is "meander", your buddy would have to make up a question like "What is the word that describes a feature of a river where it flows slowly and bends often from side to side?".

Make up 10 "answers" based on the content of the chapter or section you are using. Give this to your buddy to solve while you solve theirs.

Step 4

Construct a wordsearch of at least 10 X 10 squares. You can make it as big as you like but keep it realistic. Work together with a group of friends. Many apps allow you to make wordsearch puzzles online. The words and phrases can go in any direction and phrases can be split. Your puzzle must only contain facts linked to the topic you are revising. Your task is to find 10 bits of information to hide in your puzzle but you must not repeat information that you used in Step 3. DO NOT show where the words are. Fill up empty squares with random letters. Remember to keep a note of where your answers are hidden but do not show your friends. When you have a complete puzzle, exchange it with a friend to solve each other's puzzle.

Step 5

Now make up 10 questions (not "answers" this time) based on the same chapter used in the previous two tasks. Again, you must find NEW information that you have not yet used. Now it's getting hard to find that new information! Again, give your questions to a friend to answer.

Step 6

As you have been doing the puzzles, your brain has been actively searching for new information. Now write a NEW LIST that contains only the new information you have discovered when doing the puzzles. Your new list is the one to look at repeatedly for short bursts over the next few days. Try to remember more and more of it without looking at it. After a few days, you should be able to add words from your second list to your first list as you increase the information in your long-term memory.

FINALLY! Be inspired...

Make a list of different revision ideas and beside each one write **THINGS I HAVE** tried, **THINGS I WILL** try and **THINGS I MIGHT** try. Don't be scared of trying something new.

And remember – "FAIL TO PREPARE AND PREPARE TO FAIL!"

Intermediate 2 Chemistry

The course

The Intermediate 2 Chemistry course is made up of three units, each containing key areas. Each key area will be assessed in the exam, in either section A and/or section B.

You will have carried out nine PPA experiments; these PPAs will be assessed in section B. There will be approximately five marks that come from two or three different PPAs. The way to improve your answers to these questions is to attempt as many PPA questions from past papers as possible and use the marking instructions to check your answers.

The exam

The exam paper is set out of 80 marks, with approximately 60% for knowledge and understanding and approximately 40% for problem solving questions. There are different types of problem solving questions and they will all be assessed – selecting information, presenting information, drawing conclusions, processing information, experimental procedures, predicting and generalising. Generally, problem solving questions are well done but in experimental procedures questions, candidates commonly make the mistake of sealing tubes when drawing diagrams.

Some hints and tips

The areas that candidates find difficult are outlined below for each key area in each unit. You will always be asked some straight forward definition questions – the definition must simply be memorised.

Building Blocks Unit

(a) Substances

You need to know the names of the groups – Group 1 is the alkali metals, Group 7 is the halogens, Group 0 is the Noble gases. Also, the transition metals are found between Group 2 and Group 3.

(b) Reaction Rates

In section A, you are sometimes shown a diagram showing how energy changes during a reaction. If the energy of the products is higher than the energy of the reactants then it is an endothermic reaction – heat is taken in from the surroundings. If the energy of the products is lower than the energy of the reactants then it is an exothermic reaction – heat is given out to the surroundings.

(c) The structure of the atom

In section A, you can be asked to identify an element from its ion charge and ion electron arrangement. If the ion has a positive charge, the element has lost electrons and will be a metal. If the ion has a negative charge, the element has gained electrons and will be a non-metal. Use this information to adjust the given ion's electron arrangement to what the atom would

have. For example, if the ion has a 2+ charge and an ion electron arrangement of 2)8, then you need to add two electrons back into the electron arrangement – 2)8)2. Look up page 1 of the data booklet and you will see this is the electron arrangement for magnesium. Remember that isotopes have the same number of protons but different numbers of neutrons in their nuclei.

(d) Bonding, structure and properties

Covalent network compounds are giant structures; the formula is the simplest ratio of the atoms of each element. If given a structure, count the number of atoms of each element and cancel it down to the smallest ratio.

Candidates need to be able to draw the shape of simple 2-element compounds. Commonly questions use carbon hydride or carbon chlorides, which are both tetrahedral.

The definition of electrolytes is that they are ionic solutions that allow ions to move, completing the circuit.

(e) Chemical symbolism

Candidates need to be able to identify a diatomic molecule from a name with a prefix. Diatomic means it has two atoms, so the first thing is to change the name of the compound into a formula. Sulphur dioxide is SO_2 and therefore has three atoms (one sulphur and two oxygens); carbon monoxide is CO, has two atoms and is therefore diatomic.

A common mistake when writing a formula equation is making all elements diatomic (such as Na_2) and also giving incorrect formulae for compounds, such as magnesium oxide (Mg_2O_2).

(f) The mole

When calculating the mass of a reactant or product using a balanced equation, you must remember to use the mole ratio – it is the same as the balancing numbers given in the formula equation.

Carbon Compounds Unit

(a) Fuels

The molecule most likely to be present in petrol is octane. The definition of a combustion reaction is a reaction in which a substance burns in oxygen.

(b) Nomenclature and structural formulae

Isomers have the same molecular formula but different structures. The position of the carbon to carbon double bond in alkene and the position of the hydroxyl group in an alcohol can make it into an isomer. When drawing the structural formula of an isomer, you must take care that you make a new structure. When drawing the full structural formula of an alcohol, make sure that the bond from the oxygen goes to the carbon and not to the hydrogen.

You need to be able to identify the functional groups – ester, hydroxyl, carboxyl, amine and peptide link/amide link. The definition of a homologous series is a family of compounds that have similar chemical properties and have a general formula.

(c) Reactions of carbon compounds

A hydration reaction is an addition reaction that involves water. Water will add across the carbon to carbon double bond of an alkene to make an alcohol. In addition reactions, there could be two products and you have to be able to draw and/or name both products.

There are three families of hydrocarbons; alkanes and cycloalkanes will not decolourise bromine solution but alkenes will.

Esters are made from an alkanoic acid and an alkanol. The simplest question will ask you to name an ester from its structural formula. You also need to be able to name or draw an ester from a given acid and alkanol.

(d) Plastics and synthetic fibres

When drawing a polymer or a repeating unit from given monomers, you must put the end bonds in. You can be asked to draw the monomers from a given polymer or draw the polymer from given monomers. Candidates find condensation polymers trickier to do than addition polymers. Practise as many as possible from past papers!

You need to be able to classify a polymer as addition or condensation and identify if it is a thermoplastic or thermosetting. Always read the stem of the question as that will give you information on thermoplastic or thermosetting. If the plastic melts and can be reshaped on heating, it is a thermoplastic. If it burns on heating it is thermosetting. To decide what type of polymer it is, you need to look at the structure and see if the polymer has been made up of monomers with two functional groups per molecule – if it has then it is a condensation polymer. If not, it is an addition polymer.

(e) Natural products

Candidates must know the two substances that will hydrolyse starch – an enzyme and an acid. Being able to describe the process of photosynthesis is straightforward but you also need to know the function of chlorophyll – i.e. to trap sunlight.

Candidates can describe respiration but few are able to explain why respiration takes place – i.e. to supply energy. Proteins are polymers; amino acids are the monomers which join together, forming peptide links.

You need to know that fats are esters and when they are hydrolysed they will make fatty acids and glycerol.

Acids, Bases and Metals Unit

(a) Acids and bases

In a problem solving question, you could be asked to identify how many moles of sodium hydroxide solution will neutralise one mole of citric acid. The structure of citric acid will be given and it shows it has three –COOH groups. This means you need three moles of NaOH to neutralise it. The definition of a weak acid is one that which will only partially dissociate into ions.

(b) Salt preparation

You need to know the reactions with acids. The two that candidates find difficult are:

- a metal that reacts with an acid will make a salt and hydrogen
- a metal carbonate that reacts with an acid will make a salt, carbon dioxide and water.

A precipitation reaction is when two solutions are mixed together to form a solid. Candidates must be able to recognise this reaction from a formula equation with state symbols or from a labelled diagram of an experiment.

In titration calculations, the main errors are not applying the mole ratio or using incorrect information from the question. Take time to read the question carefully and make sure you understand the information you have been given.

(c) Metals

In displacement reactions, the metal element must be more reactive than the metal in the compound. For example, magnesium will react with zinc nitrate – magnesium is more reactive than zinc.

During electroplating, you need to remember that the object to be plated must be connected to the negative electrode of a DC power supply. This allows the positive metal ions to be attracted to it. The term used to describe a metal being extracted from its ore is a reduction reaction.

Good luck!

Remember that the rewards for passing Intermediate 2 Chemistry are well worth it! Your pass will help you get the future you want for yourself. In the exam, be confident in your own ability. If you're not sure how to answer a question trust your instincts and just give it a go anyway – keep calm and don't panic! GOOD LUCK!

[BLANK PAGE]

FOR OFFICIAL USE

Section B   **Total Marks**

X012/201

NATIONAL
QUALIFICATIONS
2009

WEDNESDAY, 3 JUNE
9.00 AM – 11.00 AM

CHEMISTRY
INTERMEDIATE 2

Fill in these boxes and read what is printed below.

Full name of centre

Town

Forename(s)

Surname

Date of birth
Day   Month   Year   Scottish candidate number   Number of seat

Necessary data will be found in the Chemistry Data Booklet for Standard Grade and Intermediate 2.

Section A — Questions 1—30 (30 marks)

Instructions for completion of **Section A** are given on page two.

For this section of the examination you must use an **HB pencil**.

Section B (50 marks)

All questions should be attempted.

The questions may be answered in any order but all answers are to be written in the spaces provided in this answer book, **and must be written clearly and legibly in ink**.

Rough work, if any should be necessary, should be written in this book, and then scored through when the fair copy has been written. If further space is required, a supplementary sheet for rough work may be obtained from the invigilator.

Additional space for answers will be found at the end of the book. If further space is required, supplementary sheets may be obtained from the invigilator and should be inserted inside the **front** cover of this booklet.

Before leaving the examination room you must give this book to the invigilator. If you do not, you may lose all the marks for this paper.

Read carefully

1 Check that the answer sheet provided is for **Chemistry Intermediate 2 (Section A)**.

2 For this section of the examination you must use an **HB pencil** and, where necessary, an eraser.

3 Check that the answer sheet you have been given has **your name**, **date of birth**, **SCN** (Scottish Candidate Number) and **Centre Name** printed on it.

   Do not change any of these details.

4 If any of this information is wrong, tell the Invigilator immediately.

5 If this information is correct, **print** your name and seat number in the boxes provided.

6 The answer to each question is **either** A, B, C or D. Decide what your answer is, then, using your pencil, put a horizontal line in the space provided (see sample question below).

7 There is **only one correct** answer to each question.

8 Any rough working should be done on the question paper or the rough working sheet, **not** on your answer sheet.

9 At the end of the exam, put the **answer sheet for Section A inside the front cover of this answer book**.

Sample Question

To show that the ink in a ball-pen consists of a mixture of dyes, the method of separation would be

        A chromatography

        B fractional distillation

        C fractional crystallisation

        D filtration.

The correct answer is **A**—chromatography. The answer **A** has been clearly marked in **pencil** with a horizontal line (see below).

Changing an answer

If you decide to change your answer, carefully erase your first answer and using your pencil, fill in the answer you want. The answer below has been changed to **D**.

SECTION A

1. Which of the following gases is a noble gas?

   A   Argon

   B   Oxygen

   C   Fluorine

   D   Nitrogen

2. Which line in the table correctly shows how the concentration of a solution changes by adding more solute or by adding more solvent?

	Adding solute	Adding solvent
A	concentration falls	concentration rises
B	concentration falls	concentration falls
C	concentration rises	concentration falls
D	concentration rises	concentration rises

3. Magnesium and zinc both react with hydrochloric acid.

   In which of the following experiments would the reaction rate be fastest?

   A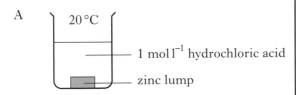
   20 °C
   1 mol l^{-1} hydrochloric acid
   zinc lump

   B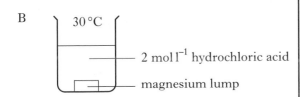
   30 °C
   2 mol l^{-1} hydrochloric acid
   magnesium lump

   C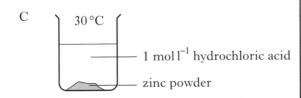
   30 °C
   1 mol l^{-1} hydrochloric acid
   zinc powder

   D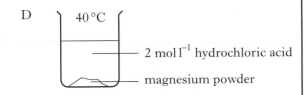
   40 °C
   2 mol l^{-1} hydrochloric acid
   magnesium powder

4. The table shows the numbers of protons, electrons and neutrons in four particles, **W**, **X**, **Y** and **Z**.

Particle	Protons	Electrons	Neutrons
W	17	17	18
X	11	11	12
Y	17	17	20
Z	18	18	18

   Which pair of particles are isotopes?

   A   **W** and **X**

   B   **W** and **Y**

   C   **X** and **Y**

   D   **Y** and **Z**

5. When solid sodium chloride dissolves in water, a solution containing sodium ions and chloride ions is formed.

   Which of the following equations correctly shows the state symbols for this process?

   A $NaCl(s) + H_2O(\ell) \rightarrow Na^+(\ell) + Cl^-(\ell)$

   B $NaCl(s) + H_2O(\ell) \rightarrow Na^+(aq) + Cl^-(aq)$

   C $NaCl(s) + H_2O(aq) \rightarrow Na^+(aq) + Cl^-(aq)$

   D $NaCl(aq) + H_2O(\ell) \rightarrow Na^+(aq) + Cl^-(aq)$

6. Metallic bonding is a force of attraction between

   A   positive ions and delocalised electrons

   B   negative ions and delocalised electrons

   C   negative ions and positive ions

   D   a shared pair of electrons and two nuclei.

   [Turn over

7. The table gives information about the attraction some atoms have for bonded electrons.

Atom	Attraction for electrons
C	least
I	
Br	↓
Cl	
F	greatest

Which of the following bonds is the **least** polar?

A   C – F

B   C – Cl

C   C – Br

D   C – I

8. Which of the following diagrams represents a **compound** made up of **diatomic** molecules?

A

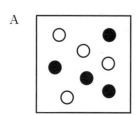

B

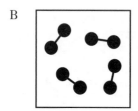

C

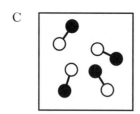

D

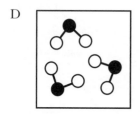

9. Which of the following diagrams could be used to represent the structure of sodium chloride?

A

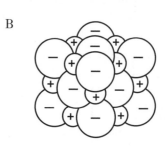

B

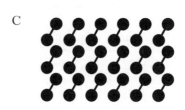

C

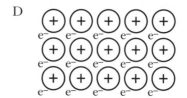

D

10.

During the electrolysis of molten copper(II) bromide

A   copper atoms lose electrons to form copper ions

B   bromine molecules gain electrons to form bromide ions

C   bromide ions gain electrons to form bromine molecules

D   copper ions gain electrons to form copper atoms.

11. What is the name of the compound with the formula Ag_2O?

    A   Silver(I) oxide

    B   Silver(II) oxide

    C   Silver(III) oxide

    D   Silver(IV) oxide

12. Which of the following exhaust emissions is most likely to come from the incomplete combustion of diesel?

    A   Water vapour

    B   Soot particles

    C   Carbon dioxide

    D   Nitrogen dioxide

13. The apparatus shown can be used to identify what is produced when a gas is burned.

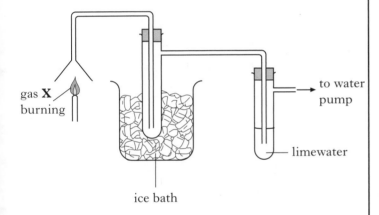

    When gas **X** was burned, a colourless liquid collected in the cooled test tube but there was no change in the limewater.

    Gas **X** could be

    A   methane

    B   carbon monoxide

    C   hydrogen

    D   ethene.

14. The fractional distillation of crude oil produces a number of different fractions.

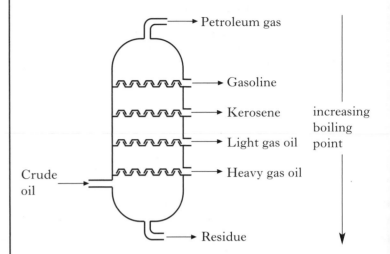

    Compared with the heavy gas oil fraction, the kerosene fraction

    A   is less flammable and contains larger hydrocarbon molecules

    B   is less flammable and contains smaller hydrocarbon molecules

    C   is more flammable and contains larger hydrocarbon molecules

    D   is more flammable and contains smaller hydrocarbon molecules.

15. Which of the following could be the molecular formula of a cycloalkane?

    A C_7H_{10}

    B C_7H_{12}

    C C_7H_{14}

    D C_7H_{16}

[Turn over

16. The shortened structural formula for an organic compound is

$$CH_3CH(CH_3)CH(OH)C(CH_3)_3.$$

Which of the following is another way of representing this structure?

A

```
        H    H   OH  CH3
        |    |    |    |
  H  —  C  — C  — C  — C  — CH3
        |    |    |    |
        H   CH3   H   CH3
```

B

```
        H    H    H   OH  CH3
        |    |    |    |    |
  H  —  C  — C  — C  — C  — C  — CH3
        |    |    |    |    |
        H    H    H    H   CH3
```

C

```
        H    H    H   CH3  CH3
        |    |    |    |    |
  H  —  C  — C  — C  — C  — C  — H
        |    |    |    |    |
        H   CH3  OH    H    H
```

D

```
        H    H    H    H    H    H
        |    |    |    |    |    |
  H  —  C  — C  — C  — C  — C  — C  — CH3
        |    |    |    |    |    |
        H   CH3  OH    H    H    H
```

17.

```
        H   OH   H    H
        |    |    |    |
  H  —  C  — C  — C  — C  — H
        |    |    |    |
        H    |    H    H
             |
        H  — C  — H
             |
             H
```

The above compound could be formed by adding water to

A

```
        H    H
        |    |
  H  —  C  — C  — C  =  C  — H
        |    |    |    |
        H    |    H    H
             |
        H  — C  — H
             |
             H
```

B

```
        H                      H
        |                      |
  H  —  C  — C  — C  =  C  — C  — H
        |    |    |    |    |
        H    |    H    H    H
             |
        H  — C  — H
             |
             H
```

C

```
        H    H    H    H
        |    |    |    |
  H  —  C  — C  — C  — C  — H
        |    |    |    |
        H    |    H    H
             |
        H  — C  — H
             |
             H
```

D

```
                       H    H
                       |    |
  H  —  C  =  C  — C  — C  — H
        |    |    |    |
        H    |    H    H
             |
        H  — C  — H
             |
             H
```

18. Part of the structure of an addition polymer is shown below. It is made using two different monomers.

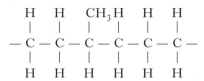

Which pair of alkenes could be used as monomers for this polymer?

A   Ethene and propene

B   Ethene and butene

C   Propene and butene

D   Ethene and pentene

19. In which of the following experiments would **both** carbohydrates give an orange precipitate when heated with Benedict's solution?

A

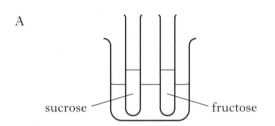

sucrose   fructose

B

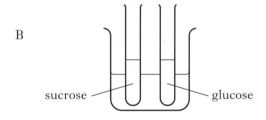

sucrose   glucose

C

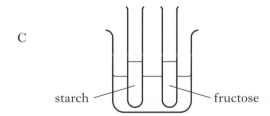

starch   fructose

D

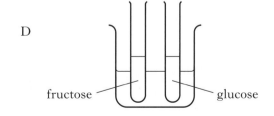

fructose   glucose

20. Glycerol can be obtained from a fat by

A   hydrolysis

B   esterification

C   condensation

D   neutralisation.

21. Which oxide, when shaken with water, would leave the pH unchanged?

(You may wish to use page 5 of the data booklet to help you.)

A   Calcium oxide

B   Carbon dioxide

C   Sulphur dioxide

D   Zinc oxide

22. Two tests were carried out on compound **X**.

Test 1

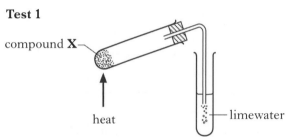

compound **X**   heat   limewater

Test 2   compound **X**

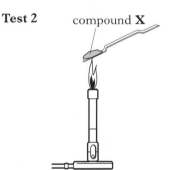

The following results were obtained.

Test	Result
1	limewater turns cloudy
2	flame turns blue-green

Which of the following could be compound **X**?

(You may wish to use page 4 of the data booklet to help you.)

A   Barium carbonate

B   Copper carbonate

C   Copper sulphate

D   Sodium sulphate

23. Which line in the table correctly shows the properties of 0.1 mol l^{-1} ethanoic acid compared to 0.1 mol l^{-1} hydrochloric acid?

	pH	Conductivity	Rate of reaction with magnesium
A	higher	lower	slower
B	lower	higher	faster
C	higher	higher	faster
D	lower	lower	slower

24. In water, an equilibrium exists between water molecules and hydrogen and hydroxide ions.

$$H_2O(\ell) \rightleftharpoons H^+(aq) + OH^-(aq)$$

At equilibrium

A   the water molecules have stopped changing into ions

B   the water molecules have all changed into ions

C   the concentrations of water molecules and ions are equal

D   the concentrations of water molecules and ions are constant.

25. $2K^+(aq) + 2I^-(aq) + Pb^{2+}(aq) + 2NO_3^-(aq)$

↓

$Pb^{2+}(I^-)_2(s) + 2K^+(aq) + 2NO_3^-(aq)$

The type of reaction represented by the equation above is

A   addition

B   neutralisation

C   precipitation

D   redox.

26. Which of the following diagrams shows the apparatus which would allow a soluble gas to be removed from a mixture of gases?

A
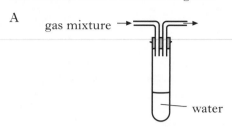

B
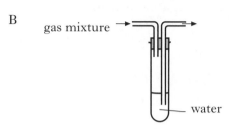

C
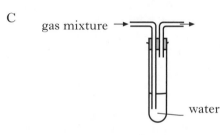

D
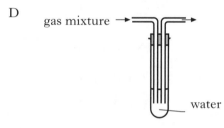

27. Which pair of metals, when connected in a cell, would give the highest voltage and a flow of electrons from **X** to **Y**?

(You may wish to use page 7 of the data booklet to help you.)

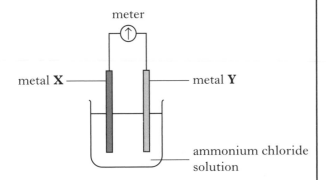

	Metal X	Metal Y
A	magnesium	copper
B	copper	magnesium
C	zinc	tin
D	tin	zinc

28. The ion-electron equation

$Ti(s) \rightarrow Ti^{2+}(aq) + 2e^-$

represents the

A reduction of titanium atoms

B reduction of titanium ions

C oxidation of titanium atoms

D oxidation of titanium ions.

29. The following statements relate to four different metals, **P**, **Q**, **R** and **S**.

Metal **P** displaces metal **Q** from a solution containing ions of **Q**.

In a cell, electrons flow from metal **S** to metal **P**.

Metal **R** is the only metal which can be obtained from its ore by heat alone.

The order of reactivity of the metals, starting with the **most** reactive is

A S, P, Q, R

B R, Q, P, S

C R, S, Q, P

D S, Q, P, R.

30.

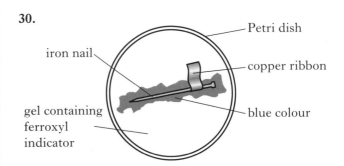

Which ion gives a blue colour with ferroxyl indicator?

A $OH^-(aq)$

B $Fe^{2+}(aq)$

C $Fe^{3+}(aq)$

D $Cu^{2+}(aq)$

Candidates are reminded that the answer sheet for Section A MUST be placed INSIDE the front cover of this answer book.

[Turn over

[BLANK PAGE]

Marks

SECTION B

50 marks are available in this section of the paper.

All answers must be written clearly and legibly in ink.

1. Atoms contain particles called protons, neutrons and electrons.

   The nuclide notation of the sodium atom is shown.

   $$^{24}_{11}\text{Na}$$

   (*a*) Complete the table to show the number of each type of particle in this sodium atom.

Particle	Number
electron	11
proton	
neutron	

   1

   (*b*) Electrons are arranged in energy levels.

   (i) Complete the diagram to show how the electrons are arranged in a sodium atom.

   (You may wish to use page 1 of the data booklet to help you.)

   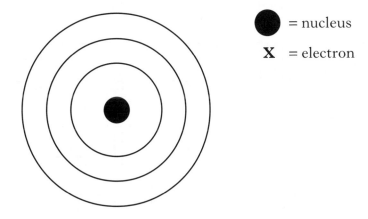

   ● = nucleus

   X = electron

   1

   (ii) Explain what holds the negatively charged electrons in place around the nucleus.

   _____

   _____

   1

   (3)

Marks

2. The diagram shows the apparatus used to prepare chlorine gas. Concentrated hydrochloric acid is reacted with potassium permanganate. The gas produced is bubbled through water to remove any unreacted hydrochloric acid and is then dried by bubbling through concentrated sulphuric acid.

   (a) Complete the diagram for the preparation of chlorine gas by adding the labels for concentrated sulphuric acid, potassium permanganate and water.

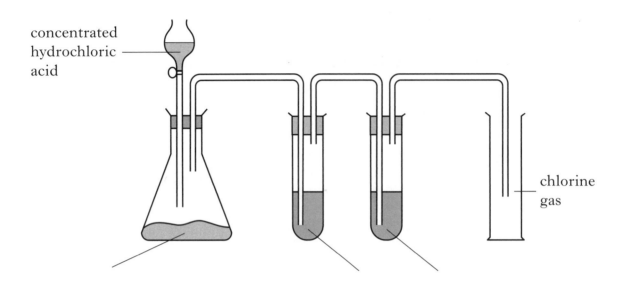

1

   (b) Chlorine is a member of the Group 7 elements.

   The graph shows the melting points of these elements.

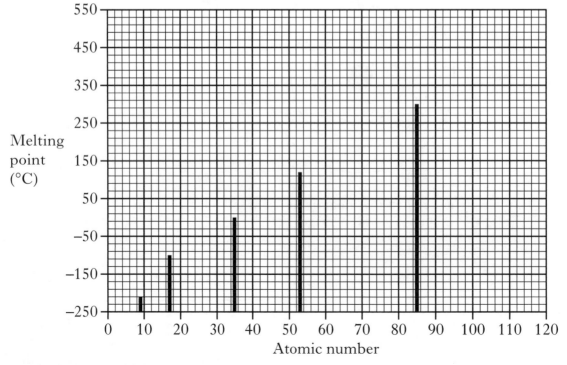

Marks

2. **(b)** **(continued)**

(i) State the relationship between the atomic number and the melting point of the Group 7 elements.

_____

_____

_____   1

(ii) The next member of this group would have an atomic number of 117.

Using the graph, predict the melting point of this element.

Melting point _____ °C   1

                                  (3)

[Turn over

Marks

3. When calcium chloride is dissolved in water, heat is released to the surroundings.

(*a*) What term is used to describe chemical reactions which give out heat?

_____ 1

(*b*) A student investigated how changing the mass of calcium chloride affects the heat released.

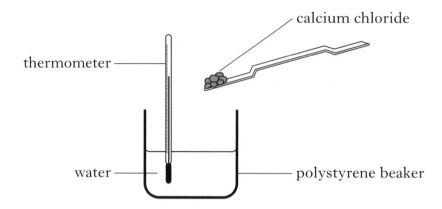

The results are shown.

Mass of calcium chloride used (g)	Highest temperature reached (°C)
0	20
5	28
10	34
15	41
20	50
25	57

Marks

3. **(b)** **(continued)**

(i) Plot a line graph of these results.

(Additional graph paper, if required, can be found on page 30.)

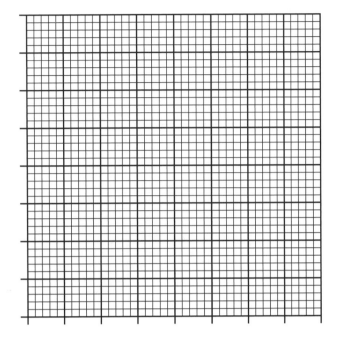

2

(ii) Using your graph, find the mass of calcium chloride that would give a temperature of 40 °C.

_____ g

1

(c) State an advantage of using a polystyrene beaker in this experiment.

_____

_____

1

(5)

[Turn over

Marks

4.   Iron is produced from iron ore in a Blast Furnace.

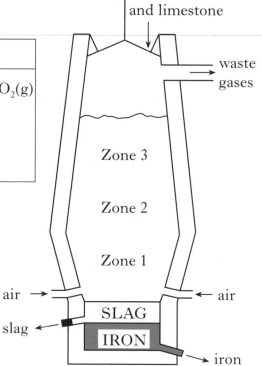

Zone	Key reaction
3	$Fe_2O_3(s) + CO(g) \rightarrow Fe(\ell) + CO_2(g)$
2	$CO_2(g) + C(s) \rightarrow 2CO(g)$
1	$C(s) + O_2(g) \rightarrow CO_2(g)$

(a)   The key reaction which takes place in Zone 3 is shown.

$$Fe_2O_3(s) + CO(g) \rightarrow Fe(\ell) + CO_2(g)$$

Balance this equation.   1

(b)   The equation for the key reaction in Zone 2 is shown below. Calculate
the mass of carbon monoxide produced when 1200 kg of carbon
reacts.

$$CO_2(g) + C(s) \rightarrow 2CO(g)$$

_____ kg   2

(c)   Why is air blown into the Blast Furnace?

_____   1

                                                                        (4)

Marks

5. Air is a mixture of gases. These gases can be separated by the process of fractional distillation.

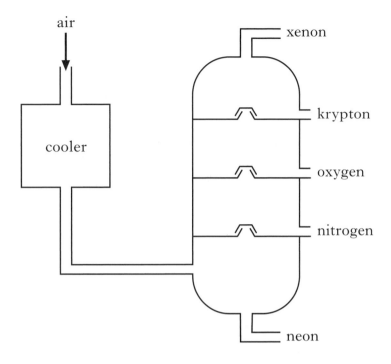

(*a*) Why can these gases be separated by fractional distillation?

_____

_____   1

(*b*) Nitrogen is separated from the mixture at −200 °C.

Circle the state that nitrogen will be in at this temperature.

(You may wish to use page 3 of your data booklet to help you.)

solid   liquid   gas   1

(*c*) The cooler contains sodium hydroxide solution. This reacts with the carbon dioxide in the air and removes it from the mixture of gases.

Name the type of chemical reaction taking place.

_____   1

                                                     (3)

[Turn over

Marks

6. The octane number of petrol is a measure of how efficiently it burns as a fuel. The higher the octane number, the more efficient the fuel.

(*a*) What is a fuel?

_____   1

(*b*) The octane numbers for some hydrocarbons are shown.

Hydrocarbon	Number of carbon atoms	Octane number
hexane	6	
heptane	7	0
octane	8	−19
2-methylpentane	6	71
2-methylhexane	7	44
2-methylheptane	8	23

(i) Predict the octane number for hexane.

_____   1

(ii) State a relationship between the structure of the hydrocarbon and their efficiency as fuels.

_____

_____

_____   1

(3)

Marks

7. The diagram shows how paraffin, $C_{12}H_{26}$, can be cracked.

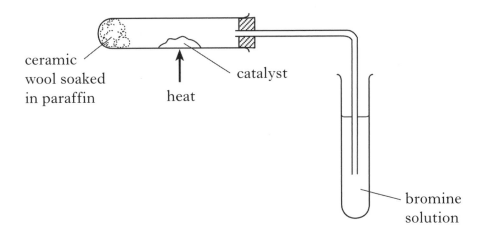

ceramic
wool soaked
in paraffin   heat   catalyst

bromine
solution

(*a*)   Name the catalyst used in cracking.

_____   1

(*b*)   One of the reactions taking place when paraffin is cracked is

$$C_{12}H_{26} \longrightarrow C_8H_{18} + \mathbf{X}$$

(i)   Identify molecule **X**.

_____   1

(ii)   Describe what would be **seen** when **X** is added to bromine
solution.

_____

_____   1

(3)

[Turn over

Marks

8. Alkynes are a homologous series of hydrocarbons which contain carbon to carbon triple bonds. Two members of this series are shown.

$$H-C\equiv C-\overset{\overset{\displaystyle H}{|}}{\underset{\underset{\displaystyle H}{|}}{C}}-\overset{\overset{\displaystyle H}{|}}{\underset{\underset{\displaystyle H}{|}}{C}}-H \qquad H-C\equiv C-\overset{\overset{\displaystyle H}{|}}{\underset{\underset{\displaystyle H}{|}}{C}}-\overset{\overset{\displaystyle H}{|}}{\underset{\underset{\displaystyle H}{|}}{C}}-\overset{\overset{\displaystyle H}{|}}{\underset{\underset{\displaystyle H}{|}}{C}}-H$$

butyne   pentyne

(a) Name the first member of this series.

_____   1

(b) Alkynes can be prepared by reacting a dibromoalkane with potassium hydroxide solution.

$$H-\overset{\overset{\displaystyle H}{|}}{\underset{\underset{\displaystyle Br}{|}}{C}}-\overset{\overset{\displaystyle H}{|}}{\underset{\underset{\displaystyle Br}{|}}{C}}-\overset{\overset{\displaystyle H}{|}}{\underset{\underset{\displaystyle H}{|}}{C}}-H \; + \; 2KOH \; \rightarrow \; H-C\equiv C-\overset{\overset{\displaystyle H}{|}}{\underset{\underset{\displaystyle H}{|}}{C}}-H \; + \; 2KBr \; + \; H_2O$$

dibromoalkane   propyne

(i) Draw a structural formula for the alkyne formed when the dibromoalkane shown reacts with potassium hydroxide solution.

$$H-\overset{\overset{\displaystyle H}{|}}{\underset{\underset{\displaystyle H}{|}}{C}}-\overset{\overset{\displaystyle H}{|}}{\underset{\underset{\displaystyle Br}{|}}{C}}-\overset{\overset{\displaystyle H}{|}}{\underset{\underset{\displaystyle Br}{|}}{C}}-\overset{\overset{\displaystyle H}{|}}{\underset{\underset{\displaystyle H}{|}}{C}}-H \; + \; 2KOH \; \rightarrow$$

1

(ii) Suggest a reason why the dibromoalkane shown below does not form an alkyne when it is added to potassium hydroxide solution.

$$H-\overset{\overset{\displaystyle H}{|}}{\underset{\underset{\displaystyle H}{|}}{C}}-\overset{\overset{\displaystyle H}{|}}{\underset{\underset{\displaystyle Br}{|}}{C}}-\overset{\overset{\displaystyle H}{|}}{\underset{\underset{\displaystyle H}{|}}{C}}-\overset{\overset{\displaystyle H}{|}}{\underset{\underset{\displaystyle Br}{|}}{C}}-\overset{\overset{\displaystyle H}{|}}{\underset{\underset{\displaystyle H}{|}}{C}}-H$$

_____

_____   1

(3)

Marks

9. The enzyme RuBisCo is one of the most abundant enzymes on Earth. It contains lysine at its active site.

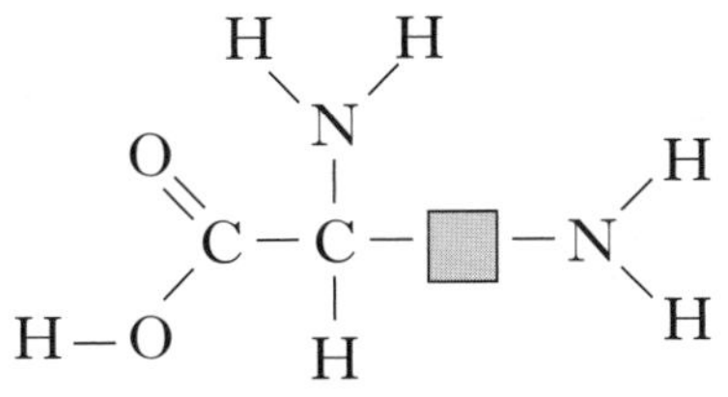

lysine

(a) Lysine contains two different types of functional groups.

Circle an amine group in the lysine molecule shown above.   **1**

(b) Name the family of compounds to which lysine belongs.

_____   **1**

(c) Complete the equation to show the structure of the other product formed when two molecules of lysine react.

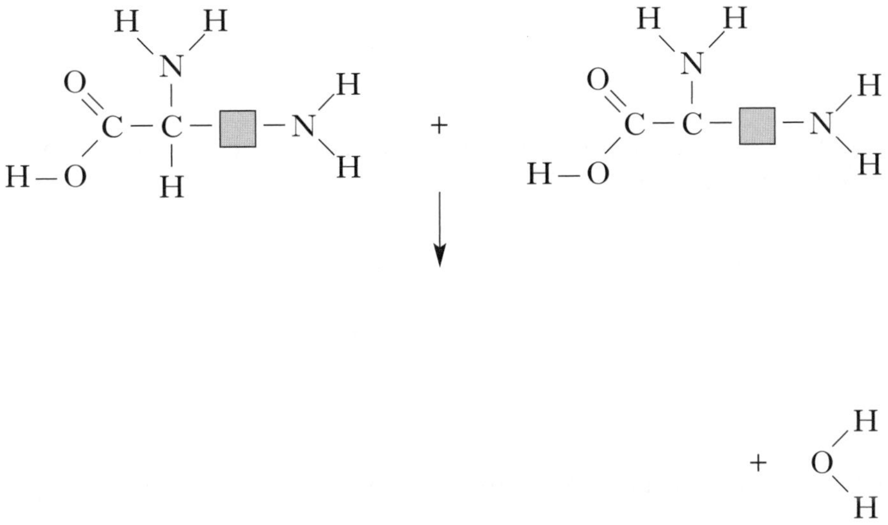

1

(3)

[Turn over

Marks

10. The flow chart shows some of the stages in the manufacture of ethanoic acid.

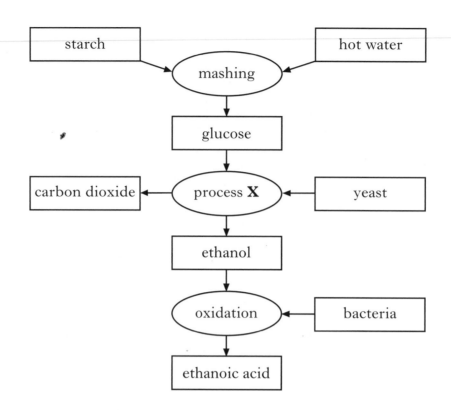

(a) In the mashing process, some of the starch is broken down into glucose.

Using the flow chart, write the word equation for the reaction taking place in the mashing process.

_____   1

(b) Name process **X**.

_____   1

(c) Draw the full structural formula for ethanoic acid.

1

(d) Ethanoic acid can be reacted with methanol to form an ester, which is used as a solvent in nail varnish remover.

Name this ester.

_____   1

(4)

Marks

11. Urea is a substance found in human urine. The enzyme urease catalyses the hydrolysis of urea. During the reaction, ammonia and carbon dioxide are produced.

$$NH_2CONH_2(aq) \quad + \quad H_2O(\ell) \quad \longrightarrow \quad 2NH_3(aq) \quad + \quad CO_2(g)$$

(*a*) What is an enzyme?

_____ 1

(*b*) The ammonia solution produced in this reaction is described as a weak base.

  (i) What is meant by a weak base?

_____

_____ 1

  (ii) The concentration of ammonia solution can be determined as follows:

    1   pipette $10\,cm^3$ of ammonia solution into a conical flask
    2   add 3 drops of indicator solution
    3   add $0{\cdot}1\,mol\,l^{-1}$ of hydrochloric acid from a burette until the indicator changes colour

  Name this technique.

_____ 1
                                        (3)

[Turn over

Marks

12. Rhubarb contains oxalic acid, $C_2H_2O_4$. Oxalic acid decolourises acidified potassium permanganate solution.

An experiment was carried out to time how long it takes to decolourise the solution using different numbers of rhubarb cubes.

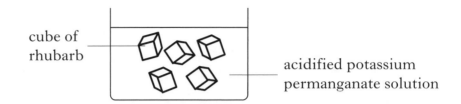

cube of rhubarb

acidified potassium permanganate solution

The results are shown.

Number of rhubarb cubes	Time to decolourise solution(s)	Relative rate (1/t) (s^{-1})
5	360	0·003
10		0·006
15	92	0·011
20	40	0·025

(a)   Calculate the time taken for 10 cubes of rhubarb to decolourise the solution.

_____ s   **1**

(b)   Using collision theory, explain why increasing the number of rhubarb cubes increases the rate of reaction.

_____

_____   **1**

Marks

12. **(continued)**

(c) The equation for the reaction between permanganate solution and the oxalic acid in rhubarb is

$$2MnO_4^- + 5C_2H_2O_4 + 6H^+ \longrightarrow 2Mn^{2+} + 10CO_2 + 8H_2O.$$
2 moles   5 moles

  (i) Calculate the number of moles of permanganate ions (MnO_4^-) in $100\,cm^3$ of a $1.0\,mol\,l^{-1}$ solution.

_____ mol   **1**

  (ii) The above equation shows that 2 moles of permanganate ions react with 5 moles of oxalic acid.

How many moles of oxalic acid $(C_2H_2O_4)$ react with $100\,cm^3$ of $1.0\,mol\,l^{-1}$ permanganate (MnO_4^-) solution?

_____ mol   **1**

                         (4)

[Turn over

Marks

13. Part of a student's PPA sheet is shown.

Intermediate 2 Chemistry	Preparation of a Salt	Unit 3 PPA1

Aim

The aim of this experiment is to make a magnesium salt by the reaction of magnesium/magnesium carbonate with sulphuric acid.

Procedure

1. Using a measuring cylinder add $20\,cm^3$ of dilute acid to the beaker.

2. Add a spatulaful of magnesium or magnesium carbonate to the acid and stir the reaction mixture with a glass rod.

3. If all the solid reacts add another spatulaful of magnesium or magnesium carbonate and stir the mixture.

4. Continue adding the magnesium or magnesium carbonate until . . .

(*a*) Complete the instruction for step 4 of the procedure.

_____

_____

_____   1

(*b*) Why is an excess of magnesium or magnesium carbonate added to the acid?

_____

_____

_____   1

(*c*) The equation for the preparation of magnesium sulphate from magnesium carbonate is shown.

$$MgCO_3(s) \;+\; H_2SO_4(aq) \;\rightarrow\; MgSO_4(aq) \;+\; \underline{\hspace{1.5cm}} \;+\; \underline{\hspace{1.5cm}}$$

Complete the equation showing the formulae for the missing products.   1

(3)

Marks

14. When iron reacts with water and oxygen, rust forms.

    The chemical name for rust is iron(III) oxide.

    (*a*) Write the chemical formula for rust.

    _____   1

    (*b*) During rusting, iron initially loses 2 electrons to form iron(II) ions. These are further oxidised to form iron(III) ions.

    Write the ion-electron equation to show iron(II) ions forming iron(III) ions.

    (You may wish to use page 7 of the data booklet to help you.)

    _____   1

    (*c*) Some iron railings were fixed into stone walls by using plugs of lead. Over time, the iron railings rusted faster at the point of contact with the lead.

    Why does lead increase the rate of rusting?

    _____

    _____   1

                                                                    (3)

[Turn over

Marks

15. The reaction between sodium hydroxide solution and dilute sulphuric acid can be followed by measuring the conductivity of the reaction mixture.

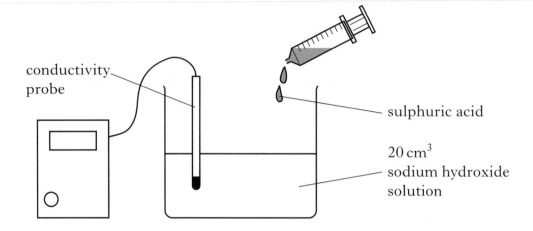

The conductivity probe measures the conductivity of the solution as the reaction proceeds.

(a) The equation for the reaction is shown.

$$2Na^+(aq) + 2OH^-(aq) + 2H^+(aq) + SO_4^{2-}(aq) \longrightarrow 2Na^+(aq) + SO_4^{2-}(aq) + 2H_2O(\ell)$$

Rewrite the equation omitting the spectator ions.

1

(b) The experiment was repeated using $20\,cm^3$ barium hydroxide solution.

The results of both experiments are shown in the table.

Solution	Conductivity at start (mA)	Conductivity at end-point (mA)
$0.1\,mol\,l^{-1}$ NaOH(aq)	80	35
$0.1\,mol\,l^{-1}$ Ba(OH)$_2$(aq)	160	0

(i) Why does barium hydroxide solution have a higher conductivity than the sodium hydroxide solution at the start?

_____

_____   1

Marks

15. **(b)** **(continued)**

The equation for the reaction between barium hydroxide solution and sulphuric acid is shown.

$$Ba^{2+}(aq) + 2OH^-(aq) + 2H^+(aq) + SO_4^{2-}(aq) \longrightarrow Ba^{2+}SO_4^{2-}(s) + 2H_2O(\ell)$$

(ii) Why is the conductivity reading at the end point 0 mA?

_____

_____   **1**

(3)

[*END OF QUESTION PAPER*]

ADDITIONAL SPACE FOR ANSWERS

ADDITIONAL GRAPH PAPER FOR QUESTION 3(b)(i)

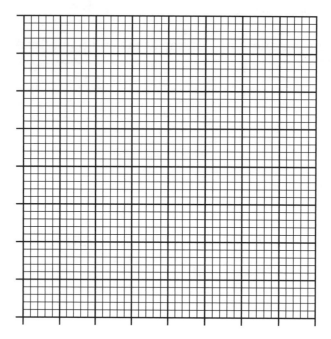

ADDITIONAL SPACE FOR ANSWERS

[BLANK PAGE]

INTERMEDIATE 2
2010

[BLANK PAGE]

FOR OFFICIAL USE

Section B   Total Marks

X012/201

NATIONAL
QUALIFICATIONS
2010

WEDNESDAY, 2 JUNE
9.00 AM – 11.00 AM

CHEMISTRY
INTERMEDIATE 2

Fill in these boxes and read what is printed below.

Full name of centre

Town

Forename(s)

Surname

Date of birth

Day   Month   Year   Scottish candidate number   Number of seat

Necessary data will be found in the Chemistry Data Booklet for Standard Grade and Intermediate 2.

Section A   Questions 1 30 (30 marks)

Instructions for completion of **Section A** are given on page two.

For this section of the examination you must use an **HB pencil**.

Section B (50 marks)

All questions should be attempted.

The questions may be answered in any order but all answers are to be written in the spaces provided in this answer book, **and must be written clearly and legibly in ink**.

Rough work, if any should be necessary, should be written in this book, and then scored through when the fair copy has been written. If further space is required, a supplementary sheet for rough work may be obtained from the Invigilator.

Additional space for answers will be found at the end of the book. If further space is required, supplementary sheets may be obtained from the Invigilator and should be inserted inside the **front** cover of this booklet.

Before leaving the examination room you must give this book to the Invigilator. If you do not, you may lose all the marks for this paper.

Read carefully

1 Check that the answer sheet provided is for **Chemistry Intermediate 2 (Section A)**.

2 For this section of the examination you must use an **HB pencil** and, where necessary, an eraser.

3 Check that the answer sheet you have been given has **your name**, **date of birth**, **SCN** (Scottish Candidate Number) and **Centre Name** printed on it.

   Do not change any of these details.

4 If any of this information is wrong, tell the Invigilator immediately.

5 If this information is correct, **print** your name and seat number in the boxes provided.

6 The answer to each question is **either** A, B, C or D. Decide what your answer is, then, using your pencil, put a horizontal line in the space provided (see sample question below).

7 There is **only one correct** answer to each question.

8 Any rough working should be done on the question paper or the rough working sheet, **not** on your answer sheet.

9 At the end of the examination, put the **answer sheet for Section A inside the front cover of this answer book**.

Sample Question

To show that the ink in a ball-pen consists of a mixture of dyes, the method of separation would be

        A chromatography

        B fractional distillation

        C fractional crystallisation

        D filtration.

The correct answer is **A**—chromatography. The answer **A** has been clearly marked in **pencil** with a horizontal line (see below).

Changing an answer

If you decide to change your answer, carefully erase your first answer and using your pencil, fill in the answer you want. The answer below has been changed to **D**.

SECTION A

1. Which of the following changes is **not** an example of a chemical reaction?

   A   Ice melting

   B   Iron rusting

   C   Methane burning

   D   Neutralising an acid

2. During the first 20 seconds of a chemical reaction, $5 \cdot 0 \, cm^3$ of gas were given off.

   The average rate of the reaction, in $cm^3 \, s^{-1}$, during the first 20 seconds is

   A $20 \cdot 0$

   B $5 \cdot 0$

   C $4 \cdot 0$

   D $0 \cdot 25$.

3. Some of the bonds in an amino acid molecule are polar covalent.

   $$H-\underset{\underset{H}{|}}{\overset{\overset{H}{|}}{N}} - \underset{\underset{H}{|}}{C} - \underset{O-H}{\overset{O}{C}}$$

   The table contains information about the attraction of some atoms for bonded electrons.

Atom	Relative attraction for bonded electrons
H	$2 \cdot 2$
C	$2 \cdot 5$
N	$3 \cdot 0$
O	$3 \cdot 5$

   The most polar bond in the amino acid molecule will be

   A $C-H$

   B $N-H$

   C $O-H$

   D $C-O$.

4. Metallic bonds are due to

   A   pairs of electrons being shared equally between atoms

   B   pairs of electrons being shared unequally between atoms

   C   the attraction of oppositely charged ions for each other

   D   the attraction of positively charged ions for delocalised electrons.

5. Which of the following elements exists as diatomic molecules?

   A   Carbon

   B   Helium

   C   Nitrogen

   D   Sulphur

6. A solution containing chloride ions, fluoride ions and bromide ions was electrolysed.

   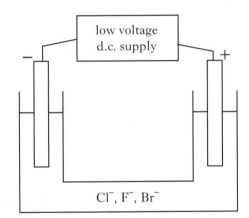

   The speed at which ions move towards an electrode depends on the size of the ion.

   The bigger the ion the slower it moves.

   The order in which the negative ions would reach the positive electrode, from first to last, is

   A Br^-, Cl^-, F^-

   B Br^-, F^-, Cl^-

   C F^-, Br^-, Cl^-

   D F^-, Cl^-, Br^-.

[Turn over

7. The formula for magnesium sulphite is

   A   MgS

   B $MgSO_3$

   C $MgSO_4$

   D MgS_2O_3.

8. $xAl(s) + yBr_2(\ell) \rightarrow zAlBr_3(s)$

   This equation will be balanced when

   A $x = 1, y = 2, z = 1$

   B $x = 2, y = 3, z = 2$

   C $x = 3, y = 2, z = 3$

   D $x = 4, y = 3, z = 4$.

9. The isotopes of carbon and oxygen are given in the table.

Isotopes of carbon	$^{12}_{6}C$	$^{13}_{6}C$	$^{14}_{6}C$
Isotopes of oxygen	$^{16}_{8}O$	$^{17}_{8}O$	$^{18}_{8}O$

   A molecule of carbon dioxide with mass 46 could contain

   A   one ^{12}C atom and two ^{16}O atoms

   B   one ^{14}C atom and two ^{18}O atoms

   C   one ^{12}C atom, one ^{16}O atom and one ^{18}O atom

   D   one ^{14}C atom, one ^{16}O atom and one ^{18}O atom.

10. 1 mole of a hydrocarbon burns completely in oxygen to produce 2 moles of carbon dioxide and 2 moles of water.

    The formula for the hydrocarbon is

    A C_2H_4

    B C_2H_6

    C C_4H_8

    D C_4H_{10}.

11. The properties of fractions obtained from crude oil depend on the sizes of molecules in the fractions.

    Compared with a fraction containing small molecules, a fraction containing large molecules will

    A   be more viscous

    B   be more flammable

    C   evaporate more readily

    D   have a lower boiling point range.

12. Which of the following hydrocarbons does **not** belong to the same homologous series as the others?

    A CH_4

    B C_3H_8

    C C_4H_{10}

    D C_6H_{12}

13. Which type of reaction is shown by the following equation?

$$H-\underset{\underset{H}{|}}{\overset{\overset{H}{|}}{C}}-\underset{\underset{H}{|}}{\overset{\overset{H}{|}}{C}}-\underset{\underset{OH}{|}}{\overset{\overset{H}{|}}{C}}-H \rightarrow H-\underset{\underset{H}{|}}{\overset{\overset{H}{|}}{C}}-\overset{\overset{H}{|}}{C}=\overset{\overset{H}{|}}{C}-H + H_2O$$

    A   Condensation

    B   Dehydration

    C   Hydration

    D   Hydrolysis

14. Which of the following polymers dissolves in water?

    A   Kevlar

    B   Perspex

    C   Poly(ethene)

    D   Poly(ethenol)

15. The structure below shows a section of an addition polymer.

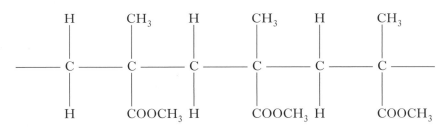

Which molecule is used to make this polymer?

A
$$CH_3 \quad\quad H$$
$$C = C$$
$$H \quad\quad COOCH_3$$

B
$$H \quad\quad CH_3$$
$$C = C$$
$$H \quad\quad COOCH_3$$

C
$$CH_3 \quad\quad COOCH_3$$
$$C = C$$
$$H \quad\quad H$$

D
$$H \quad\quad CH_3$$
$$H - C - C - H$$
$$H \quad\quad COOCH_3$$

---

16. Which of the following groups can react together to form an amide (peptide) link?

A $-O-H$ and $\overset{H}{\underset{H}{>}}N-$

B $-O-H$ and $\overset{O}{\underset{H-O}{\diagup\!\!\!\diagup}}C-$

C $-N\overset{H}{\underset{H}{\diagdown}}$ and $\overset{O}{\underset{H-O}{\diagup\!\!\!\diagup}}C-$

D $-N\overset{H}{\underset{H}{\diagdown}}$ and $\overset{H}{\underset{H}{>}}N-$

17. When a reversible reaction is at equilibrium, the concentrations of reactants and products are

A   constant but not equal

B   constant and equal

C   not constant but equal

D   not constant and not equal.

18. Which of the following substances dissolves in water to give a solution of pH greater than 7?

A   Ammonia

B   Carbon dioxide

C   Sulphur dioxide

D   Sodium chloride

[Turn over

19. An acidic solution contains

    A   only hydrogen ions

    B   more hydrogen ions than hydroxide ions

    C   more hydroxide ions than hydrogen ions

    D   equal numbers of hydrogen ions and hydroxide ions.

20. What mass of ammonium sulphate, $(NH_4)_2SO_4$, is required to produce 0·5 litres of a $1 \text{ mol } l^{-1}$ solution?

    A   32 g

    B   64 g

    C   66 g

    D   132 g

21. Which line in the table correctly shows the properties of $0·1 \text{ mol } l^{-1}$ hydrochloric acid when compared with $0·1 \text{ mol } l^{-1}$ ethanoic acid?

	pH	Conductivity	Rate of reaction with magnesium
A	lower	lower	slower
B	higher	higher	faster
C	lower	higher	faster
D	higher	lower	slower

22. Which of the following potassium compounds is a base?

    A   Potassium nitrate

    B   Potassium chloride

    C   Potassium sulphate

    D   Potassium carbonate

23. In a neutralisation reaction between an acid and an alkali, the pH

    A   of the acid increases

    B   of the acid is unchanged

    C   of the alkali increases

    D   of the alkali is unchanged.

24. Which of the following substances will **not** produce a gas when added to dilute hydrochloric acid?

    A   Copper

    B   Zinc

    C   Copper carbonate

    D   Zinc carbonate

25. Which salt can **not** be prepared by a precipitation reaction?

(You may wish to use the data booklet to help you.)

    A   Barium sulphate

    B   Lead(II) sulphate

    C   Calcium chloride

    D   Silver chloride

26. The equation for the reaction between lead(II) nitrate and sodium iodide is:

$$Pb^{2+}(aq) + 2NO_3^-(aq) + 2Na^+(aq) + 2I^-(aq)$$
$$\downarrow$$
$$Pb^{2+}(I^-)_2(s) + 2Na^+(aq) + 2NO_3^-(aq)$$

The spectator ions present in this reaction are

    A $Na^+(aq)$ and $NO_3^-(aq)$

    B $Na^+(aq)$ and $I^-(aq)$

    C $Pb^{2+}(aq)$ and $NO_3^-(aq)$

    D $Pb^{2+}(aq)$ and $I^-(aq)$.

27. Which metal will displace zinc from a solution of zinc sulphate?

    A   Iron

    B   Magnesium

    C   Silver

    D   Tin

28. The ion-electron equation for the oxidation and reduction steps in the reaction between magnesium and silver(I) ions are:

$$Mg \rightarrow Mg^{2+} + 2e^-$$
$$Ag^+ + e^- \rightarrow Ag$$

The overall redox equation is

A $\quad Mg + 2Ag^+ \rightarrow Mg^{2+} + 2Ag$

B $\quad Mg + Ag^+ \rightarrow Mg^{2+} + Ag$

C $\quad Mg + Ag^+ + e^- \rightarrow Mg^{2+} + Ag + 2e^-$

D $\quad Mg + 2Ag \rightarrow Mg^{2+} + 2Ag^+$.

29. Aluminium can be extracted from aluminium oxide by

A heating alone

B heating with carbon

C heating with carbon monoxide

D electrolysis.

30. An iron nail is covered with water.

Which of the following would increase the rate at which the iron nail rusts?

A Adding glucose to the water

B Wrapping magnesium around the nail

C Adding potassium nitrate to the water

D Attaching the nail to the negative terminal of a d.c. power supply

Candidates are reminded that the answer sheet for Section A MUST be placed INSIDE the front cover of this answer book.

[Turn over

[BLANK PAGE]

Marks

SECTION B

50 marks are available in this section of the paper.

All answers must be written clearly and legibly in ink.

1. Elements are made up of atoms.

   An atom of an element is represented by the diagram below.

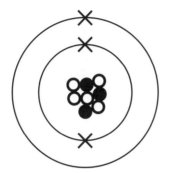

● = protons

○ = neutrons

✗ = electrons

   (*a*) What name is given to the part of the atom which contains protons and neutrons?

   _____ 1

   (*b*) Using the information in the diagram:

      (i) state the mass number of this atom;

      _____ 1

     (ii) explain why this atom is electrically neutral;

      _____

      _____ 1

    (iii) name the **family** of elements to which this atom belongs.

      _____ 1

      (4)

[Turn over

Marks

2. Cool packs can be used to treat some sports injuries.

The pack contains solid ammonium nitrate and water in two separate compartments. When the pack is squeezed the ammonium nitrate dissolves in the water forming a solution. This results in a drop in temperature.

(a) What term is used to describe a reaction in which there is a drop in temperature?

_____   1

(b) The equation for the reaction taking place in the cool pack is shown.

$NH_4NO_3(\quad)$ + $H_2O(\quad)$ → $NH_4NO_3(\quad)$

Complete the equation by adding state symbols.   1

(c) What name is given to a liquid, such as water, that can be used to dissolve substances?

_____   1

(d) The change in temperature in the cool pack can be calculated using the equation below.

$$\text{Temperature change} = \frac{\text{energy change (kJ)}}{\text{mass of water (kg)} \times 4 \cdot 2}$$

Calculate the temperature change using the following information.

Energy change (kJ)	6·72
Mass of water (kg)	0·2

_____ °C   1

(4)

Marks

3. The element carbon can exist in the form of diamond.

The structure of diamond is shown in the diagram.

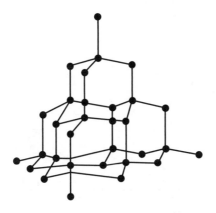

(a) Name the type of **bonding** and **structure** present in diamond.

_____   1

(b) Carbon forms many compounds with other elements such as hydrogen.

   (i) Draw a diagram to show how the outer electrons are arranged in a
   molecule of methane, CH_4.

   1

   (ii) Draw a diagram to show the **shape** of a molecule of methane,
   CH_4.

   1

   (3)

4. Gold is a very soft metal. In order to make it harder, goldsmiths mix it with silver. The quality of the gold is indicated in carats.

(a) The graph shows information about the quality of gold.

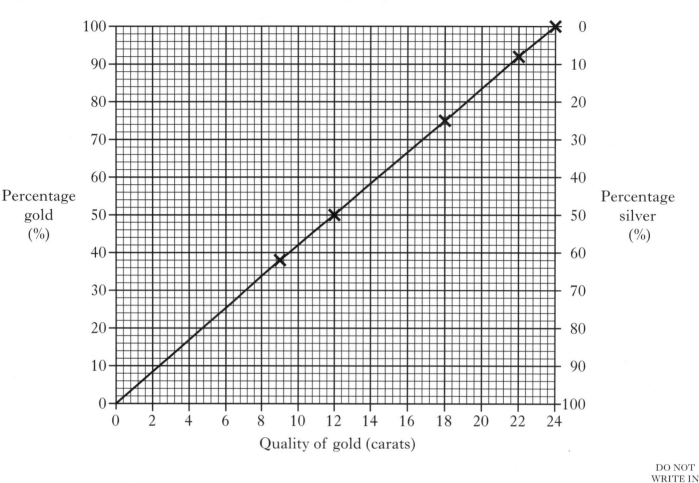

Marks

(i) What is the percentage of silver in an 18 carat gold ring?

_____ %

1

(ii) Calculate the mass of silver in an 18 carat gold ring weighing 6 g.

_____ g   **1**

Marks

4. (continued)

(b) Silver tarnishes in air forming black silver sulphide, Ag_2S.

The equation for the reaction is:

$$4Ag + 2H_2S + O_2 \longrightarrow 2Ag_2S + 2H_2O$$

What mass of silver sulphide would be formed from $1 \cdot 08\,g$ of silver?

2

(4)

[Turn over

Marks

5. The diagram below shows the apparatus used in the **PPA**, **"Cracking"**.

mineral wool
soaked in
liquid paraffin

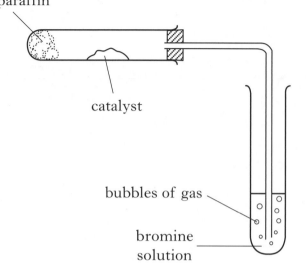

catalyst

bubbles of gas

bromine
solution

(a) Describe how the bunsen burner is used to heat the apparatus.

_____

_____   1

(b) Explain why the delivery tube must be removed from the bromine solution before heating is stopped.

_____

_____   1

(c) (i) Name the catalyst that is used in this cracking reaction.

_____   1

(ii) Catalysts speed up the rate of a reaction without being used up.
State another reason for using a catalyst.

_____   1

(d) One of the reactions taking place is:

$$CH_2CHCH_3 + Br_2 \longrightarrow CH_2BrCHBrCH_3$$

What name is given to this type of chemical reaction?

_____   1

(5)

Marks

6. Chemicals in food provide flavour and smell. Ketones are responsible for the flavour in blue cheese.

Two examples of ketones are shown below.

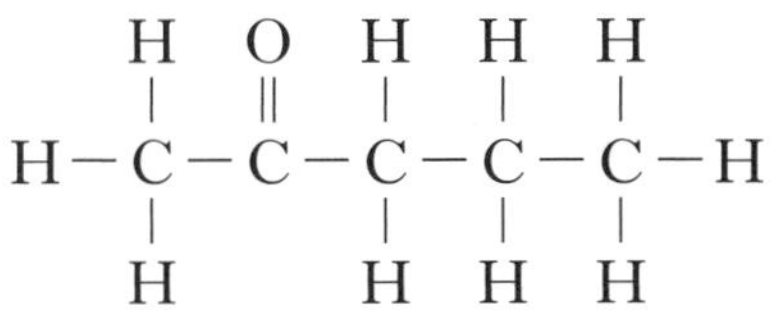

```
    H  O  H  H  H              H  H  O  H  H
    |  ||  |  |  |             |  |  ||  |  |
H − C − C − C − C − C − H    H − C − C − C − C − C − H
    |     |  |  |             |  |     |  |
    H     H  H  H             H  H     H  H
```

       pentan-2-one 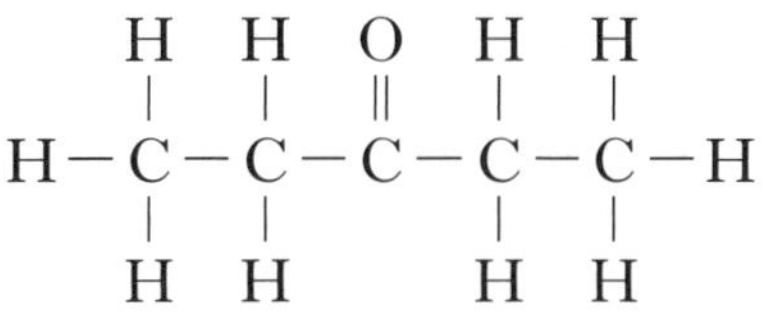   pentan-3-one

(a) Draw a structure for hexan-3-one.

1

(b) Suggest a name for the ketone shown below.

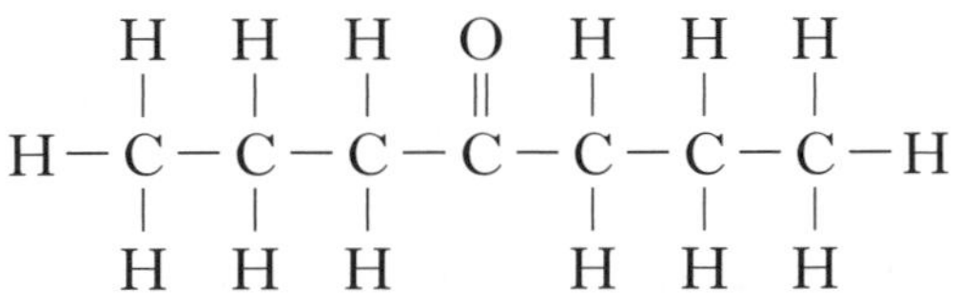

```
    H  H  H  O  H  H  H
    |  |  |  ||  |  |  |
H − C − C − C − C − C − C − C − H
    |  |  |     |  |  |
    H  H  H     H  H  H
```

_____ 1

(c) Information about the boiling points of four ketones is shown in the table.

Ketone	Boiling point (°C)
C_3H_6O	56
C_4H_8O	80
$C_5H_{10}O$	102
$C_6H_{12}O$	127

Predict the boiling point of $C_7H_{14}O$.

_____ °C

1

(3)

[Turn over

Marks

7. A recipe for making blackcurrant wine is shown.

---

1. Boil 4 litres of water and add 2 kg of sugar.

2. Stir until all the sugar dissolves.

3. Add 1·5 kg of crushed blackcurrants and let the mixture cool to room temperature.

4. Add some yeast.

5. Cover the container and leave it in a warm place for 5 days.

6. Filter the mixture into a glass jar and fit an airlock.

7. Leave the mixture for 3 months before filtering and bottling.

(a) Yeast is used to convert sugar into ethanol.

   (i) What name is given to this process?

   _____   1

   (ii) What **type** of substance, found in yeast, acts as a catalyst?

   _____   1

(b) Why was the mixture cooled at step 3, before the yeast was added to it?

   _____

   _____   1

(c) When blackcurrant brandy is made from blackcurrant wine, the ethanol concentration is increased.

   How could this be done?

   _____   1

   (4)

DO NOT WRITE IN THIS MARGIN

Marks

8. Sweets, such as pineapple cubes, contain the artificial flavouring methyl butanoate.

(*a*) To which family of compounds does methyl butanoate belong?

______________________________ **1**

(*b*) Methyl butanoate can be broken down to form an alkanol and an alkanoic acid.

(i) Name this type of chemical reaction.

______________________________ **1**

(ii) Draw the full structural formula for the alkanoic acid formed from the breakdown of methyl butanoate.

1

(3)

[Turn over

Marks

9.

> **Autumn days**
>
> Adapted from an article by Victoria Ashton
>
> September 2001
>
> The leaves of a Beech tree contain three coloured pigments; chlorophyll which is green, carotenes which are yellow and tannins which are brown.
>
> In summer, the leaves are green as they contain a lot of chlorophyll. The chlorophyll is involved in converting water and carbon dioxide into glucose and oxygen. The glucose formed can then be converted into starch by condensation polymerisation.
>
> In autumn the chlorophyll is broken down, supplying the tree with essential magnesium ions (Mg^{2+}) which it will need over the winter. As a result, the colours of the carotenes and tannins dominate in autumn, giving the Beech tree its golden yellow coloured leaves.

(a) What name is given to the process, in which water and carbon dioxide are converted into glucose and oxygen?

_____   **1**

(b) State a test and the result that you would get, which would distinguish between glucose and starch.

_____

_____   **1**

(c) The structure of a tannin molecule is shown below.

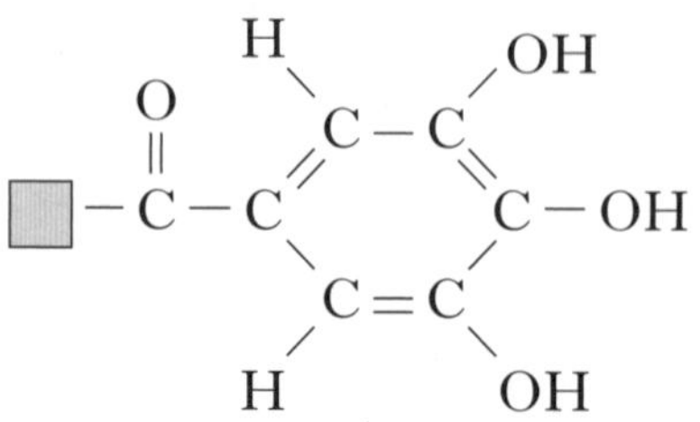

Circle a hydroxyl group in this structure.   **1**

(d) What is the electron arrangement for a magnesium ion, Mg^{2+}?

_____   **1**

(4)

Marks

10. People often drink lemonade to quench their thirst.

(*a*) Lemonade contains citric acid.

Suggest a pH value for lemonade.

_____   1

(*b*) To make the drink fizzy, carbon dioxide gas is added to the lemonade. The solubility of carbon dioxide gas depends on the temperature of the lemonade.

The graph shows how the solubility of carbon dioxide gas changes with temperature.

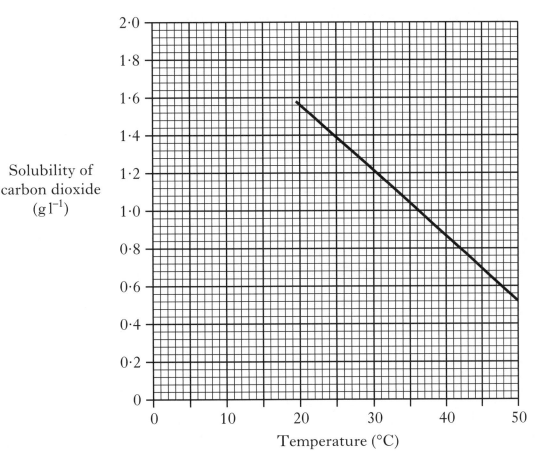

(i) Write a general statement describing the effect of temperature on the solubility of carbon dioxide gas.

_____

_____   1

(ii) Use the graph to predict the solubility of carbon dioxide at 10 °C.

_____ $g\,l^{-1}$ 1

(3)

Marks

11. Slaked lime can be added to lochs to reduce acidity.

(*a*) What causes the lochs to become acidic?

_____   1

(*b*) Slaked lime can be made from limestone.

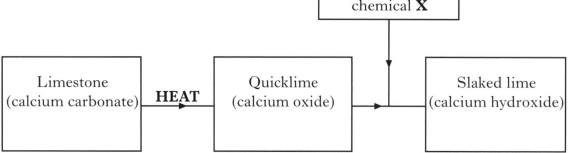

(i) Name the elements present in calcium carbonate.

_____   1

(ii) Suggest a name for chemical **X**.

_____   1

(3)

Marks

12. Lamp posts made of iron or steel can have different coatings to prevent rusting.

(a) Some lamp posts are coated in a layer of paint.

How does the layer of paint prevent the iron lamp post from rusting?

_____

_____ 1

(b) Lamp posts can also be coated by dipping them in molten zinc.

   (i) What term is used to describe this process?

_____ 1

   (ii) Why does the iron not rust even when the zinc coating is scratched?

_____

_____ 1

                                     (3)

[Turn over

Marks

13. Sodium sulphate crystals can be made from sodium hydroxide solution and dilute sulphuric acid as shown in the procedure below.

Step 1

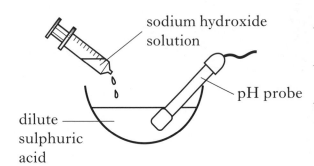

Add sodium hydroxide solution to dilute sulphuric acid until

_____

_____

_____

Step 2

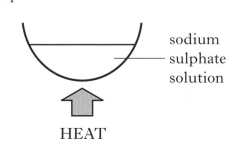

HEAT

Evaporate until half of the solution remains.

Step 3

Leave until the remaining water evaporates.

Step 4

Sodium sulphate crystals are formed.

(*a*) Complete the instructions for Step 1.   1

DO NOT WRITE IN THIS MARGIN

Marks

13. (continued)

(*b*) The equation for the reaction is:

$$H_2SO_4 \quad + \quad 2NaOH \longrightarrow Na_2SO_4 \quad + \quad 2H_2O$$

In the experiment 50 cm^3 of sodium hydroxide solution reacted with 20 cm^3 0·1 $mol\,l^{-1}$ dilute sulphuric acid.

Calculate the concentration of the sodium hydroxide solution.

______________ $mol\,l^{-1}$ **2**

(3)

[Turn over

Marks

14. (*a*) In a **PPA**, a student was asked to investigate if the type of electrolyte used affects the voltage produced in a cell.

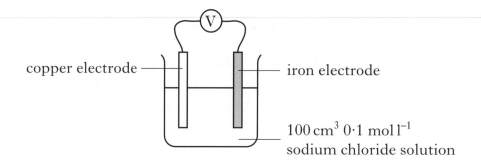

copper electrode — iron electrode

$100\,cm^3$ $0{\cdot}1\,mol\,l^{-1}$
sodium chloride solution

(i) Complete the labelling of a second cell which could be used to compare the effect of changing the electrolyte from sodium chloride to hydrochloric acid.

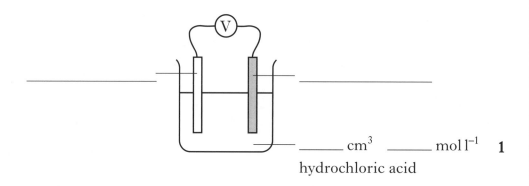

_____ cm^3 _____ $mol\,l^{-1}$ **1**
hydrochloric acid

(ii) What is done during this PPA to make sure the results are reliable?

_____   **1**

Marks

14. (continued)

(*b*) Cells can also be made in which both metals and non-metals are used.

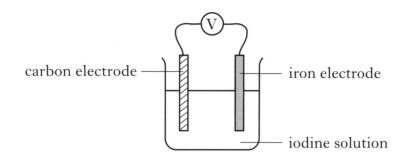

(i) The ion-electron equation for the reaction taking place at the carbon electrode is:

$$I_2(aq) \quad + \quad 2e^- \quad \longrightarrow \quad 2I^-(aq)$$

On the diagram clearly mark the path and direction of electron flow.

1

(ii) What property of carbon makes it suitable for use as an electrode?

_____ 1

(4)

[END OF QUESTION PAPER]

DO NOT
WRITE IN
THIS
MARGIN

ADDITIONAL SPACE FOR ANSWERS

INTERMEDIATE 2

2011

HODDER
GIBSON
LEARN MORE

[BLANK PAGE]

FOR OFFICIAL USE

Section B   Total Marks

X012/201

NATIONAL QUALIFICATIONS 2011

THURSDAY, 26 MAY 1.00 PM – 3.00 PM

CHEMISTRY INTERMEDIATE 2

Fill in these boxes and read what is printed below.

Full name of centre

Town

Forename(s)

Surname

Date of birth

Day   Month   Year   Scottish candidate number   Number of seat

Necessary data will be found in the Chemistry Data Booklet for Standard Grade and Intermediate 2.

Section A – Questions 1–30 (30 marks)

Instructions for completion of **Section A** are given on page two.

For this section of the examination you must use an **HB pencil**.

Section B (50 marks)

All questions should be attempted.

The questions may be answered in any order but all answers are to be written in the spaces provided in this answer book, **and must be written clearly and legibly in ink**.

Rough work, if any should be necessary, should be written in this book, and then scored through when the fair copy has been written. If further space is required, a supplementary sheet for rough work may be obtained from the Invigilator.

Additional space for answers will be found at the end of the book. If further space is required, supplementary sheets may be obtained from the Invigilator and should be inserted inside the **front** cover of this booklet.

Before leaving the examination room you must give this book to the Invigilator. If you do not, you may lose all the marks for this paper.

Read carefully

1 Check that the answer sheet provided is for **Chemistry Intermediate 2 (Section A)**.

2 For this section of the examination you must use an **HB pencil** and, where necessary, an eraser.

3 Check that the answer sheet you have been given has **your name**, **date of birth**, **SCN** (Scottish Candidate Number) and **Centre Name** printed on it.

   Do not change any of these details.

4 If any of this information is wrong, tell the Invigilator immediately.

5 If this information is correct, **print** your name and seat number in the boxes provided.

6 The answer to each question is **either** A, B, C or D. Decide what your answer is, then, using your pencil, put a horizontal line in the space provided (see sample question below).

7 There is **only one correct** answer to each question.

8 Any rough working should be done on the question paper or the rough working sheet, **not** on your answer sheet.

9 At the end of the examination, put the **answer sheet for Section A inside the front cover of this answer book**.

Sample Question

To show that the ink in a ball-pen consists of a mixture of dyes, the method of separation would be

        A chromatography

        B fractional distillation

        C fractional crystallisation

        D filtration.

The correct answer is **A**—chromatography. The answer **A** has been clearly marked in **pencil** with a horizontal line (see below).

Changing an answer

If you decide to change your answer, carefully erase your first answer and using your pencil, fill in the answer you want. The answer below has been changed to **D**.

SECTION A

1. Which of the following compounds contains both a transition metal ion and a halide ion?

   A   Aluminium bromide

   B   Cobalt chloride

   C   Iron oxide

   D   Sodium fluoride

2. Which of the following compounds contains only two elements?

   A   Magnesium hydroxide

   B   Magnesium phosphate

   C   Magnesium sulphite

   D   Magnesium nitride

3. A student investigated the reaction between marble chips and excess dilute hydrochloric acid.

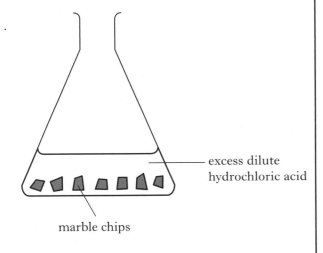

excess dilute hydrochloric acid

marble chips

   Which of the following would **not** affect the rate of the reaction?

   A   Increasing the volume of the acid

   B   Decreasing the size of the marble chips

   C   Decreasing the concentration of the acid

   D   Increasing the temperature of the acid

4. Which line in the table describes a **neutron**?

	Mass	Charge
A	1	−1
B	negligible	0
C	1	+1
D	1	0

5. An atom has 26 protons, 26 electrons and 30 neutrons. The atom has

   A   atomic number 26, mass number 56

   B   atomic number 56, mass number 30

   C   atomic number 30, mass number 26

   D   atomic number 52, mass number 56.

6. Excess magnesium is burned in an enclosed volume of air.

   Which line in the table best describes the gas after burning is complete?

	Oxygen	Nitrogen	Carbon dioxide
A	1%	98%	0·03%
B	1%	79%	19%
C	16%	79%	4%
D	20%	79%	0·03%

7. Copper is a good conductor of electricity because

   A   the atoms are free to vibrate

   B   the atoms are in close contact

   C   the atoms have the electron arrangement 2, 8, 18, 1

   D   electrons can move readily from one atom to the next.

[Turn over

8. What is the charge on the chromium ion in $CrCl_3$?

   A   1+

   B   1–

   C   3+

   D   3–

9. What name is given to the reaction shown by the following equation?

   $$C_6H_{12}O_6 + 6O_2 \rightarrow 6CO_2 + 6H_2O$$

   A   Combustion

   B   Condensation

   C   Dehydration

   D   Hydrolysis

10. The fractional distillation of crude oil depends on the fact that different hydrocarbons have different

    A   densities

    B   solubilities

    C   boiling points

    D   ignition temperatures.

11. Which of the following molecules would most likely be present in petrol?

    A CH_4

    B C_3H_8

    C C_8H_{18}

    D $C_{14}H_{30}$

12. Which of the following compounds belongs to the same homologous series as the compound with the molecular formula C_3H_8?

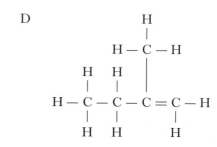

13.

    The name of the above compound is

    A   but-2-ene

    B   pent-2-ene

    C   but-3-ene

    D   pent-3-ene.

14. When propene undergoes an addition reaction with hydrogen bromide, two products are formed.

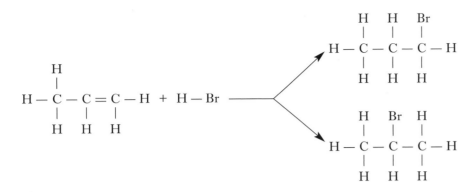

Which of the following alkenes will also produce **two** products when it undergoes an addition reaction with hydrogen bromide?

A   Ethene

B   But-1-ene

C   But-2-ene

D   Hex-3-ene

15. The table shows the result of heating two compounds with acidified potassium dichromate solution.

Compound	Acidified potassium dichromate solution
H—C—C—C—C—H (with H, H, O(double bond), H substituents)	stays orange
H—C—C—C—C—H (with H, H, H, O(double bond) substituents)	turns green

Which of the following compounds will **not** turn acidified potassium dichromate solution green?

A

$$H-\overset{\displaystyle H}{\underset{\displaystyle H}{C}}-\overset{\displaystyle O}{C}-\overset{\displaystyle H}{\underset{\displaystyle H}{C}}-H$$

B

$$H-\overset{\displaystyle H}{\underset{\displaystyle H}{C}}-\overset{\displaystyle H}{\underset{\displaystyle H}{C}}-\overset{\displaystyle O}{C}-H$$

C

$$H-\overset{\displaystyle H}{\underset{\displaystyle H}{C}}-\overset{\displaystyle O}{C}-H$$

D

$$\overset{\displaystyle O}{H-C-H}$$

16. $C_6H_{12}O_6$ $C_{12}H_{22}O_{11}$

The above compounds are

A   isomers

B   hydrocarbons

C   alkanols

D   carbohydrates.

17.   What functional group is **always** found in a protein molecule?

A $-N\begin{smallmatrix}H\\ \\H\end{smallmatrix}$

B $\begin{smallmatrix}\diagdown & & \diagup\\ & C=C & \\ \diagup & & \diagdown\end{smallmatrix}$

C
$$\begin{matrix} & O & H \\ & \| & | \\ -C & - & N- \end{matrix}$$

D
$$\begin{matrix} & O & & \\ & \| & & | \\ -C & - & O & -C- \\ & & & | \end{matrix}$$

18.   Which of the following are polymers?

A   Plant sugars

B   Animal fats

C   Marine oils

D   Vegetable proteins

19.   Fats and oils are essential in the diet.

Which line in the table best describes an oil?

	Degree of unsaturation	Melting point
A	high	relatively high
B	high	relatively low
C	low	relatively high
D	low	relatively low

20.   When one molecule of fat is completely hydrolysed, the number of ester links broken is

A   1

B   2

C   3

D   4.

21.   Which of the following oxides dissolves in water to produce a solution with a pH greater than 7?

A Na_2O

B Al_2O_3

C SO_2

D Ag_2O

22.   Which line in the table describes what happens to a dilute solution of hydrochloric acid when water is added to it?

	pH	H^+(aq) concentration
A	increases	increases
B	increases	decreases
C	decreases	increases
D	decreases	decreases

23.   Which of the following solutions has the highest pH?

A $0{\cdot}1$ mol l^{-1} ammonia

B $0{\cdot}1$ mol l^{-1} hydrochloric acid

C $0{\cdot}1$ mol l^{-1} sodium chloride

D $0{\cdot}1$ mol l^{-1} sodium hydroxide

24.   Which of the following pairs of chemicals react to produce a gas that turns lime water milky?

A   Calcium carbonate and dilute hydrochloric acid

B   Copper oxide and dilute sulphuric acid

C   Copper and dilute hydrochloric acid

D   Magnesium and dilute sulphuric acid

25. $H^+(aq) + NO_3^-(aq) + K^+(aq) + OH^-(aq) \longrightarrow K^+(aq) + NO_3^-(aq) + H_2O$

The spectator ions in the reaction are

A $H^+(aq)$ and $K^+(aq)$

B $NO_3^-(aq)$ and $OH^-(aq)$

C $H^+(aq)$ and $OH^-(aq)$

D $K^+(aq)$ and $NO_3^-(aq)$.

26. Which of the following metals would react with zinc chloride solution?

(You may wish to use page 7 of the data booklet to help you.)

A   Copper

B   Gold

C   Iron

D   Magnesium

27.

Metal	Reaction with	
	Dilute acid	Water
X	reacts	no reaction
Y	no reaction	no reaction
Z	reacts	reacts

Which of the following shows the metals in order of **increasing** reactivity?

A   **X Y Z**

B   **Y X Z**

C   **Z X Y**

D   **Z Y X**

28. Some metals can be obtained from their metal oxides by heat alone.

Which of the following oxides would produce a metal when heated?

A   Calcium oxide

B   Copper oxide

C   Zinc oxide

D   Silver oxide

29. For iron to rust

A   only water must be present

B   only oxygen must be present

C   both water and oxygen must be present

D   oxygen, water and salt must be present.

30. The coatings on four strips of iron were scratched to expose the iron. The strips were placed in salt solution.

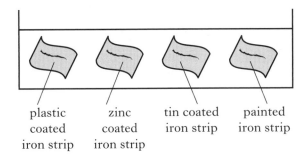

plastic coated iron strip   zinc coated iron strip   tin coated iron strip   painted iron strip

Which iron strip would have rusted most quickly?

A   Plastic coated

B   Zinc coated

C   Tin coated

D   Painted

Candidates are reminded that the answer sheet for Section A MUST be placed INSIDE the front cover of this answer book.

[BLANK PAGE]

DO NOT
WRITE IN
THIS
MARGIN

SECTION B

Marks

50 marks are available in this section of the paper.

All answers must be written clearly and legibly in ink.

1. The properties of a substance depend on its type of bonding and structure.

   There are four types of bonding and structure.

Discrete covalent molecular	Covalent network	Ionic lattice	Metallic lattice

   (a) Complete the table to match up each type of bonding and structure with its properties.

Bonding and structure type	Properties
	do not conduct electricity and have high melting points
	have high melting points and conduct electricity when liquid but not when solid
	conduct electricity when solid and have a wide range of melting points
	do not conduct electricity and have low melting points

2

   (b) A section of a covalent network compound is shown below.

   ● = silicon

   ○ = oxygen

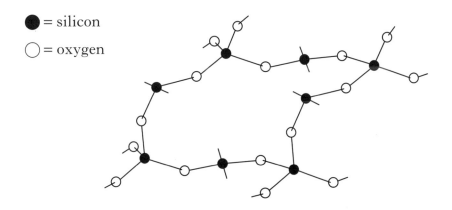

   Write the formula for this covalent network compound.

   _____

1

(3)

DO NOT
WRITE IN
THIS
MARGIN

Marks

2.   Information on some two-element molecules is shown in the table.

Name	Formula	Shape of molecule
hydrogen fluoride	HF	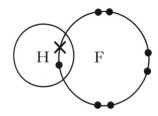
water	H_2O	
ammonia	NH_3	

(a) Complete the table to show the **shape** of a molecule of ammonia.   1

(b) The hydrogen fluoride molecule can be represented as:

Showing **all** outer electrons, draw a similar diagram to represent a molecule of water, H_2O.

1

(2)

Marks

3. Hydrogen peroxide is a useful bleaching agent and is contained in many hair dyes. Over time, the hair dye becomes less effective as the hydrogen peroxide decomposes forming water and oxygen.

   The equation for the decomposition of hydrogen peroxide is:

   $$H_2O_2(aq) \longrightarrow O_2(g) \ + \ H_2O(\ell)$$

   (a) Balance this equation.   1

   (b) The above reaction is often used to make oxygen in the laboratory. To speed up the reaction, the catalyst manganese dioxide is added.

   Complete the diagram to show how the oxygen can be collected.

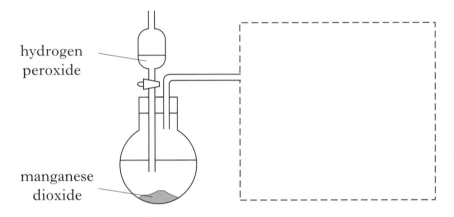

   hydrogen peroxide

   manganese dioxide   1

   (c) State the test for oxygen gas.   1

   _____

   (d) When 34 g of hydrogen peroxide decomposes, 12 litres of oxygen is produced.

   Calculate the volume of oxygen produced when 1·7 g of hydrogen peroxide decomposes.

   _____ litres   1

                                                                               (4)

Marks

4. Research is being carried out into making chemicals that can be used to help relieve the side effects of chemotherapy.

   Part of the process is shown.

   chemical **A** + hydrogen $\xrightarrow{\text{catalyst}}$ chemical **B**

   (a) (i) This reaction is catalysed using the homogeneous catalyst, ruthenium(II) chloride.

   What is meant by a homogeneous catalyst?

   _____

   _____   1

   (ii) Write the formula for ruthenium(II) chloride.

   1

   (b) As the reaction proceeds the hydrogen is used up and the pressure decreases.

Time (min)	0	5	10	15	20	30	35	45
Decrease in pressure (bar)	0	0·6	1·2	1·7	2·2	2·9	3·1	3·1

Marks

4. (*b*) (continued)

(i) Draw a line graph showing the decrease in pressure as time proceeds.

(Additional graph paper, if required, will be found on *Page twenty-six*.)

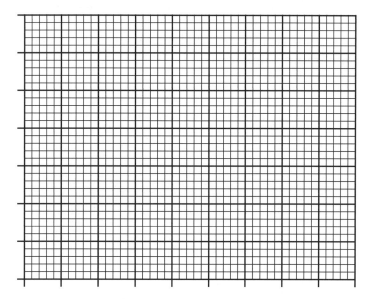

2

(ii) Using your graph, at what time did the reaction finish?

_____ min   1

(iii) Calculate the average rate of the reaction, in bar min^{-1}, between 10 and 20 minutes.

_____ bar min^{-1} 1

(6)

DO NOT WRITE IN THIS MARGIN

Marks

5. Ammonium sulphate is a commonly used fertiliser. It can be produced by the reaction between ammonium carbonate and calcium sulphate.

$$(NH_4)_2CO_3(aq) + CaSO_4(aq) \longrightarrow (NH_4)_2SO_4(aq) + CaCO_3(s)$$

(*a*) Name this type of chemical reaction.

______________________________ **1**

(*b*) What mass of ammonium carbonate, $(NH_4)_2CO_3$, would be needed to make 13·2 kg of ammonium sulphate, $(NH_4)_2SO_4$?

__________ kg **2**

(3)

Marks

6. In the **PPA "Hydrolysis of starch"**, dilute hydrochloric acid can be used to break down starch.

A section of a student's workcard is shown.

1. Set up the experiment as shown in the diagram.

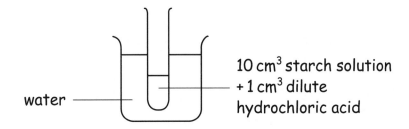

2. Boil the water in the beaker for 5 minutes and then turn off the Bunsen burner.

3. Add a small amount of solid sodium hydrogencarbonate to the test tube.

4. Add $5\,cm^3$ of Benedict's solution to the test tube and warm gently.

5. Observe and record your results.

(a) After heating with dilute hydrochloric acid, solid sodium hydrogencarbonate is added to the reaction mixture.

Why is sodium hydrogencarbonate needed?

_____

_____ 1

(b) A control experiment is used in this PPA.

Label the diagram to show this control experiment.

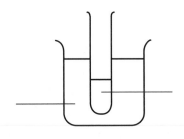

1

(2)

Marks

7. When marking a student's report on plastics, the teacher circled three errors.

The marked report is shown.

> Most plastics are made from chemicals which come from [1]coal.
>
> Plastics are made when monomers polymerise to form polymers.
>
> Some common plastics are polystyrene, poly(ethene) and Biopol:
>
> * Polystyrene is made from the monomer [2]propene
> * Poly(ethene) is a thermoplastic
> * [3]Biopol is a plastic which is soluble in water.

Correct the circled errors.

1 _____

2 _____

3 _____

(3)

Marks

8. Many different gases are found in car exhaust fumes. Some of these gases are produced by the combustion of petrol in car engines.

The pie chart shows the gases present in the exhaust fumes of a car.

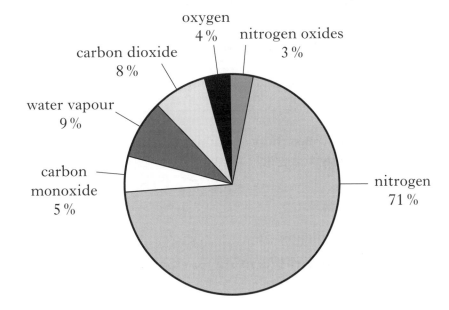

(a) What evidence in the pie chart shows that incomplete combustion of petrol has taken place?

_____   1

(b) The car's exhaust fumes were found to contain 3% nitrogen oxides.

Predict the percentage of nitrogen oxides that could be found in the exhaust fumes if the car was fitted with a catalytic convertor.

_____ %   1

(c) The burning of some fuels releases sulphur dioxide into the atmosphere.

Why is this a problem?

_____

_____   1

(3)

Marks

9.

The little pen-tailed tree shrew, found in the jungles of West Malaysia, feeds on nectar from the Bertam palm tree. This nectar contains glucose which ferments, producing solutions of up to 3·8% alcohol. Therefore, the tree shrew regularly drinks a solution which is equivalent to a man drinking 9 units of alcohol per day. It seems that the tree shrew never gets drunk because it is able to breakdown the alcohol much quicker than humans can.

(a) Name the process by which plants make glucose from carbon dioxide and water.

_____   1

(b) What **type** of substance must be present in the nectar to allow the fermentation of glucose to take place?

_____   1

(c) The alcohol produced is ethanol.

Draw the **shortened structural formula** for ethanol.

1

(d) Using information in the passage above, calculate the volume of alcohol solution the tree shrew drinks each day.

$$\text{Volume of alcohol solution} = \frac{\text{units of alcohol} \times 1\cdot25}{\text{\% of alcohol}}$$

_____ cm^3 1

(4)

Marks

10. Synthetic nappies contain hydrogel polymers which attract and absorb water molecules.

(a) The following is part of the structure of a hydrogel polymer.

```
    H       COOH  H       COOH  H       COOH
    |       |     |       |     |       |
————C———————C—————C———————C—————C———————C————
    |       |     |       |     |       |
    H       H     H       H     H       H
```

(i) Draw the monomer from which this polymer is made.

1

(ii) The diagram below shows how water molecules are attracted to the hydrogel.

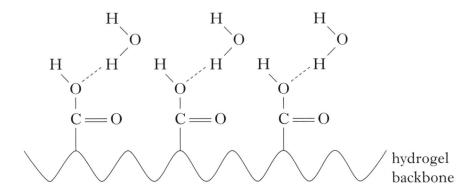

What type of bonding must be present **in the water molecules**, which allows them to be attracted to the hydrogel?

_____ 1

(b) Many hydrogels are polymers of carboxylic acids. Carboxylic acids are weak acids.

What is meant by a **weak** acid?

_____

_____ 1

(3)

Marks

11.   Many different molecules give us different smells and tastes.

(a)   The following molecule gives a "fishy" smell.

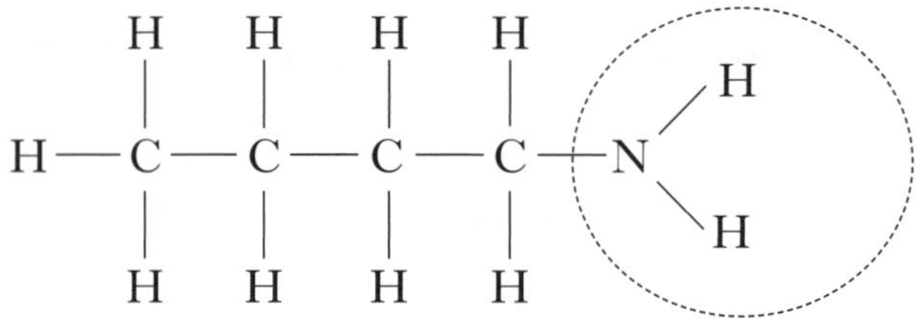

Name the functional group circled in this molecule.

_____   1

(b)   Artificial flavourings added to foods are often esters.

The following ester gives an orange flavour.

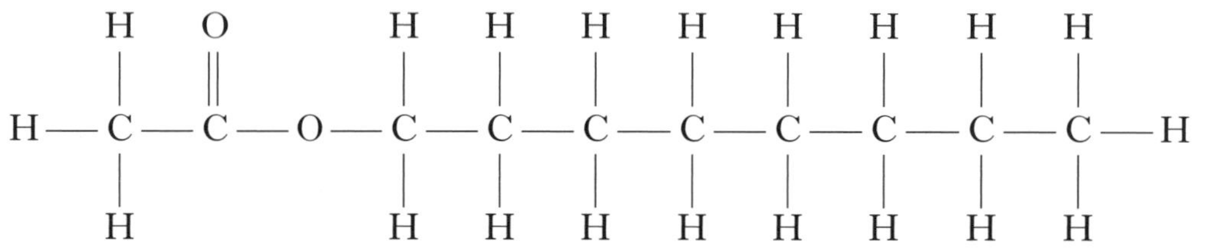

Name this ester.

_____   1

(c)   Some household cleaners contain the chemical limonene which gives them a lemon smell. The structure of limonene is shown below.

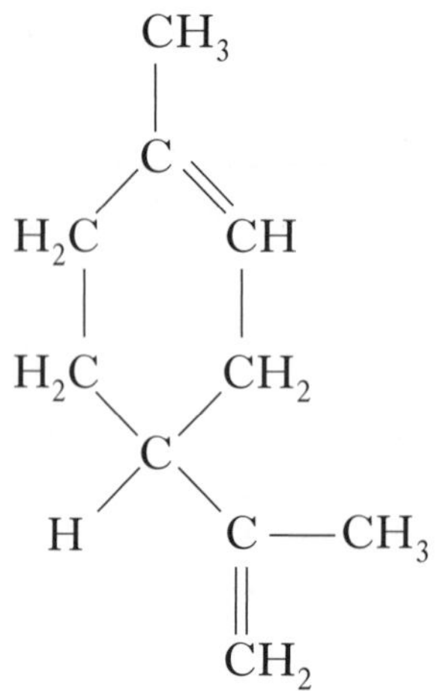

11. **(c)** **(continued)**   *Marks*

Using bromine solution, a student carried out titrations to determine the concentration of limonene in a household cleaner.

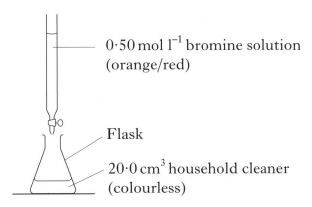

0·50 mol l^{-1} bromine solution (orange/red)

Flask

20·0 cm^3 household cleaner (colourless)

Titration	Initial burette reading (cm^3)	Final burette reading (cm^3)	Titre (cm^3)
1	0·5	17·1	16·6
2	0·2	16·3	16·1
3	0·1	16·0	15·9

(i) What colour change would be seen in the flask that indicates the end point of the titrations?

_____ to _____   **1**

(ii) What average volume should be used in calculating the concentration of limonene?

_____ cm^3 **1**

(iii) The equation for the reaction between limonene and bromine solution is shown.

$$C_{10}H_{16}(aq) \ + \ 2Br_2(aq) \ \longrightarrow \ C_{10}H_{16}Br_4(aq)$$

Calculate the concentration of limonene in the household cleaner.

_____ mol l^{-1} **2**

(6)

Marks

12. Metals can be extracted from metal compounds by heat alone, heating with carbon or by electrolysis.

(*a*) Name the type of chemical reaction which takes place when a metal is extracted from its compound.

_____   1

(*b*) In a **PPA**, a solution of copper(II) chloride was electrolysed.

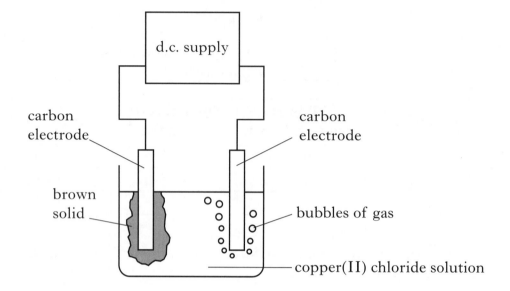

(i) Complete the table by adding the charge for each electrode.

Observation at _____ electrode	Observation at _____ electrode
bubbles of gas	brown solid formed

1

(ii) How could the gas be identified?

_____

_____   1

(3)

DO NOT
WRITE IN
THIS
MARGIN

Marks

13. Some indicators can have different colours when in solutions of different pH values.

    The tables give information about two indicators, bromothymol blue and methyl orange.

Bromothymol blue	
Colour	**pH**
yellow	below 6·0
blue	above 7·6

Methyl orange	
Colour	**pH**
red	below 3·1
yellow	above 4·4

The pH of three solutions was investigated using both indicators.

The results are shown below.

Substance	Colour with bromothymol blue	Colour with methyl orange
A	yellow	red
B	yellow	yellow
C	blue	yellow

(a) Which solution is alkaline?

    Solution _____

    1

(b) Suggest a pH value for solution B.

    pH _____

    1

    (2)

[Turn over

Marks

14. The voltage obtained when different pairs of metal strips are connected in a cell varies and this leads to the electrochemical series.

Using the apparatus below, a student investigated the electrochemical series. Copper and four other metal strips were used in this investigation.

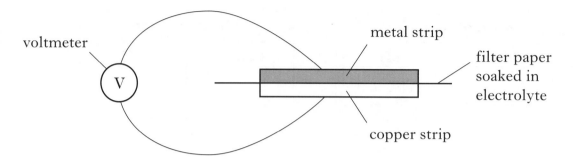

The results are shown.

Metal strip	Voltage (V)	Direction of electron flow
1	0·6	metal 1 to copper
2	0·2	copper to metal 2
3	0·9	metal 3 to copper
4	0·1	copper to metal 4

(a) Which of the metals used is highest in the electrochemical series?

metal _____   1

(b) Which **two** of the metals used would produce the highest voltage when connected in a cell?

metal _____ and metal _____   1

(c) What would be the reading on the voltmeter if both strips of metal were copper?

_____ V   1

(d) Why can glucose solution **not** be used as the electrolyte?

_____   1

                                                                 (4)

Marks

15. Fizzy drinks contain acids.

These acids can attack the compound calcium hydroxyapatite which is found in tooth enamel.

The equation for the reaction is:

$$Ca_{10}(PO_4)_6(OH)_2(s) + 8H^+(aq) \longrightarrow 6CaHPO_4(s) + 4Ca^{2+}(aq) + 2H_2O(\ell)$$

calcium hydroxyapatite

(*a*) What will happen to the pH as the tooth enamel is attacked by the acids?

_____   1

(*b*) Fluoride prevents tooth decay by replacing the hydroxide ions of calcium hydroxyapatite with fluoride ions to form hard wearing calcium fluoroapatite.

calcium hydroxyapatite $\xrightarrow{\text{fluoride ions}}$ calcium fluoroapatite
$Ca_{10}(PO_4)_6(OH)_2$

Write the formula for calcium fluoroapatite.

1
(2)

[END OF QUESTION PAPER]

ADDITIONAL SPACE FOR ANSWERS

ADDITIONAL GRAPH PAPER FOR QUESTION 4(b)(i)

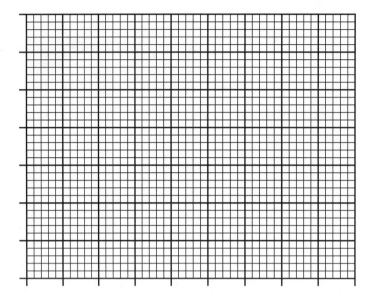

ADDITIONAL SPACE FOR ANSWERS

[BLANK PAGE]

INTERMEDIATE 2

2012

[BLANK PAGE]

FOR OFFICIAL USE

Section B   Total Marks

X012/11/02

NATIONAL QUALIFICATIONS 2012

MONDAY, 14 MAY 1.00 PM – 3.00 PM

CHEMISTRY INTERMEDIATE 2

Fill in these boxes and read what is printed below.

Full name of centre

Town

Forename(s)

Surname

Date of birth

| Day | Month | Year | Scottish candidate number | Number of seat |

Necessary data will be found in the Chemistry Data Booklet for Standard Grade and Intermediate 2.

Section A – Questions 1–30 (30 marks)

Instructions for completion of **Section A** are given on page two.

For this section of the examination you must use an **HB pencil**.

Section B (50 marks)

All questions should be attempted.

The questions may be answered in any order but all answers are to be written in the spaces provided in this answer book, **and must be written clearly and legibly in ink**.

Rough work, if any should be necessary, should be written in this book, and then scored through when the fair copy has been written. If further space is required, a supplementary sheet for rough work may be obtained from the Invigilator.

Additional space for answers will be found at the end of the book. If further space is required, supplementary sheets may be obtained from the Invigilator and should be inserted inside the **front** cover of this booklet.

Before leaving the examination room you must give this book to the Invigilator. If you do not, you may lose all the marks for this paper.

Read carefully

1 Check that the answer sheet provided is for **Chemistry Intermediate 2 (Section A)**.

2 For this section of the examination you must use an **HB pencil** and, where necessary, an eraser.

3 Check that the answer sheet you have been given has **your name**, **date of birth**, **SCN** (Scottish Candidate Number) and **Centre Name** printed on it.

   Do not change any of these details.

4 If any of this information is wrong, tell the Invigilator immediately.

5 If this information is correct, **print** your name and seat number in the boxes provided.

6 The answer to each question is **either** A, B, C or D. Decide what your answer is, then, using your pencil, put a horizontal line in the space provided (see sample question below).

7 There is **only one correct** answer to each question.

8 Any rough working should be done on the question paper or the rough working sheet, **not** on your answer sheet.

9 At the end of the examination, put the **answer sheet for Section A inside the front cover of this answer book**.

Sample Question

To show that the ink in a ball-pen consists of a mixture of dyes, the method of separation would be

   A chromatography

   B fractional distillation

   C fractional crystallisation

   D filtration.

The correct answer is **A**—chromatography. The answer **A** has been clearly marked in **pencil** with a horizontal line (see below).

Changing an answer

If you decide to change your answer, carefully erase your first answer and using your pencil, fill in the answer you want. The answer below has been changed to **D**.

A   B   C   D

SECTION A

1. An element, **X**, has the following properties.

   • It is a gas.

   • It is **not** made up of molecules.

   • It does **not** react with other elements.

   Element, **X**, is likely to be in group

   A   0

   B   1

   C   2

   D   7.

2. Which of the following would react fastest with $2 \, mol \, l^{-1}$ hydrochloric acid?

   A   Magnesium ribbon

   B   Magnesium powder

   C   Zinc ribbon

   D   Zinc powder

3. The diagram shows the energy changes during a reaction.

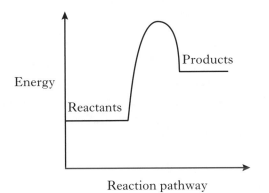

   Which of the following statements is true?

   A   The reaction is endothermic.

   B   Energy is given out to the surroundings.

   C   The reaction is exothermic.

   D   The products have less energy than the reactants.

4. Which of the following numbers is the same for lithium and oxygen atoms?

   A   Mass number

   B   Atomic number

   C   Number of outer electrons

   D   Number of occupied energy levels

5. Atoms of an element form ions with a single positive charge and an electron arrangement of 2, 8.

   The element is

   A   fluorine

   B   lithium

   C   sodium

   D   neon.

6. Which of the following substances is made up of molecules containing polar covalent bonds?

   A   Calcium oxide

   B   Chlorine

   C   Sodium bromide

   D   Water

7. Which of the following pairs of elements combine to form an ionic compound?

   A   Lead and fluorine

   B   Sulphur and oxygen

   C   Carbon and nitrogen

   D   Phosphorus and chlorine

8. Which of the following compounds exists as diatomic molecules?

   A   Carbon monoxide

   B   Sulphur dioxide

   C   Nitrogen trihydride

   D   Carbon tetrachloride

[Turn over

9. The shapes and names of some molecules are shown below.

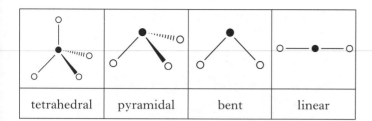

tetrahedral	pyramidal	bent	linear

Phosphine is a compound of phosphorus and hydrogen. The shape of a molecule of phosphine is likely to be

A   tetrahedral

B   pyramidal

C   bent

D   linear.

10. Solid ionic compounds do not conduct electricity because

A   the ions are not free to move

B   the electrons are not free to move

C   solid substances never conduct electricity

D   there are no charged particles in ionic compounds.

11. Which of the following alkanes will produce 3 moles of carbon dioxide when 1 mole of it is completely burned?

A   Ethane

B   Propane

C   Butane

D   Pentane

12. Fractional distillation of crude oil produces a number of different fractions.

Which of the following properties apply to a fraction containing large hydrocarbon molecules?

A   High viscosity and low flammability

B   Low viscosity and low flammability

C   High viscosity and high flammability

D   Low viscosity and high flammability

13. The following structure represents an amine called ethylmethylamine:

$$H-N \begin{array}{l} CH_3 \\ C_2H_5 \end{array}$$

Another amine has the following structure:

$$H-N \begin{array}{l} CH_3 \\ C_3H_7 \end{array}$$

This amine is called

A   methylamine

B   butylamine

C   propylamine

D   methylpropylamine.

14. The structure of citric acid is

$$
\begin{array}{c}
H \\
| \\
H-C-COOH \\
| \\
HO-C-COOH \\
| \\
H-C-COOH \\
| \\
H
\end{array}
$$

How many moles of sodium hydroxide would be required to exactly neutralise **one** mole of citric acid?

A   1

B   2

C   3

D   4

15. $C_8H_{18} \xrightarrow{\text{Process X}}$ Ethene + Compound Y

Which line in the table correctly identifies Process X and Compound Y?

	Process X	Compound Y
A	cracking	hexane
B	cracking	hexene
C	distillation	hexane
D	distillation	hexene

16.   Polyethene terephthalate (PET) is used to make plastic bottles which can easily be recycled by heating and reshaping.

A section of the PET structure is shown.

$-\overset{O}{\overset{\|}{C}}-\bigcirc-\overset{O}{\overset{\|}{C}}-O-CH_2-CH_2-O-\overset{O}{\overset{\|}{C}}-\bigcirc-\overset{O}{\overset{\|}{C}}-$

Which line in the table best describes PET?

	Type of polymer	Property
A	addition	thermoplastic
B	condensation	thermosetting
C	addition	thermosetting
D	condensation	thermoplastic

17.   Part of a polymer structure is shown.

$$\begin{array}{cccccc} CH_3 & H & CH_3 & H & CH_3 & H \\ | & | & | & | & | & | \\ -C & -C & -C & -C & -C & -C- \\ | & | & | & | & | & | \\ H & CN & H & CN & H & CN \end{array}$$

Which of the following gases could **not** be produced when this polymer is burned?

A   CO

B CO_2

C   HCl

D   HCN

18.   Which of the following plastics could be used to make a soluble coating for a dishwasher tablet?

A   PVC

B   Biopol

C   Polystyrene

D   Poly(ethenol)

19.   Which compound could be obtained by the hydrolysis of a fat?

A   Ethanol

B   Glucose

C   Glycerol

D   Propanol

20.   To which class of compounds does the hormone insulin belong?

A   Carbohydrates

B   Fats

C   Proteins

D   Hydrocarbons

21.   What is the most likely pH value that would be obtained when zinc oxide is added to water?

(You may wish to use page 5 of the data booklet to help you.)

A   5

B   7

C   9

D   11

22.   Reactions can be represented using ionic equations. Which ionic equation shows a neutralisation reaction?

A $2H_2O(\ell) + O_2(g) + 4e^- \longrightarrow 4OH^-(aq)$

B $H^+(aq) + OH^-(aq) \longrightarrow H_2O(\ell)$

C $SO_2(g) + H_2O(\ell) \longrightarrow 2H^+(aq) + SO_3^{2-}(aq)$

D $NH_4^+(s) + OH^-(s) \longrightarrow NH_3(g) + H_2O(\ell)$

[Turn over

23. Four cells were made by joining copper, iron, magnesium and zinc to silver. The four cells produced the following voltages 0·5 V, 0·9 V, 2·7 V and 1·1 V.

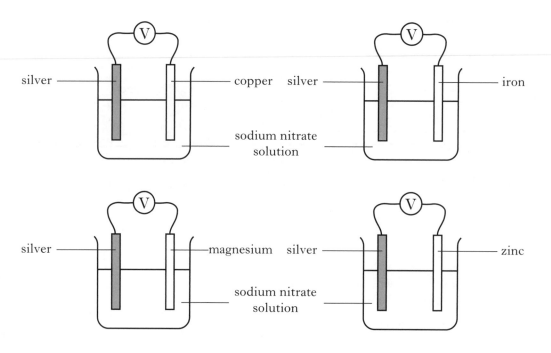

Which of the following will be the voltage of the cell containing silver joined to copper?

(You may wish to use page 7 of the data booklet to help you.)

A   0·5 V

B   0·9 V

C   1·1 V

D   2·7 V

24. Which acidic gas is produced by the sparking of air?

A   Carbon dioxide

B   Sulphur dioxide

C   Nitrogen dioxide

D   Hydrogen chloride

25. A student adds a powder to dilute hydrochloric acid. A gas which burns with a pop is produced.

The powder could be

A   carbon

B   calcium oxide

C   sodium carbonate

D   zinc.

26. Which of the following substances is **not** a salt?

A   Copper sulphate

B   Sodium oxide

C   Magnesium chloride

D   Calcium nitrate

27. In which of the following test tubes will a reaction occur?

A

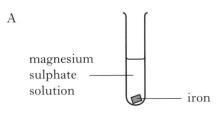

magnesium sulphate solution — iron

B

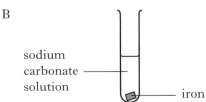

sodium carbonate solution — iron

C

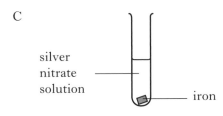

silver nitrate solution — iron

D

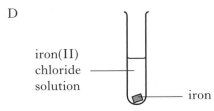

iron(II) chloride solution — iron

28.

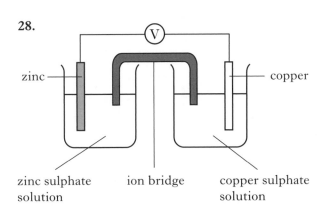

zinc — copper

zinc sulphate solution   ion bridge   copper sulphate solution

Which line in the table is correct for the above cell?

	Zinc electrode	Copper electrode
A	mass increases	mass increases
B	mass increases	mass decreases
C	mass decreases	mass decreases
D	mass decreases	mass increases

29. A metal can be extracted from its ore by heating the ore with carbon but **not** by heating the ore on its own.

The position of the metal in the reactivity series is most likely to be between

(You may wish to use page 7 of the data booklet to help you.)

A   zinc and magnesium

B   magnesium and potassium

C   zinc and copper

D   copper and gold.

30. In which of the following experiments would the iron nail **not** rust?

A

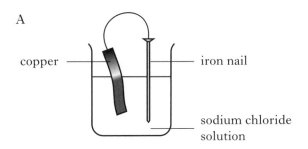

copper — iron nail

sodium chloride solution

B

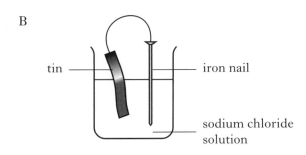

tin — iron nail

sodium chloride solution

C

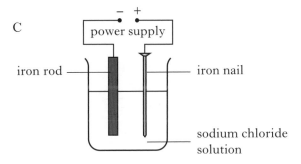

power supply

iron rod — iron nail

sodium chloride solution

D

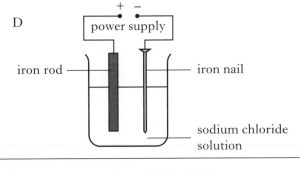

power supply

iron rod — iron nail

sodium chloride solution

Candidates are reminded that the answer sheet for Section A MUST be placed INSIDE the front cover of this answer book.

[BLANK PAGE]

SECTION B

Marks

50 marks are available in this section of the paper.

All answers must be written clearly and legibly in ink.

1. Glass is made from the chemical silica, SiO_2, which is covalently bonded and has a melting point of 1700 °C.

   (a) What does the melting point of silica suggest about its **structure**?

   _____   1

   (b) Antimony(III) oxide is added to reduce any bubbles that may appear during the manufacturing process.

   Write the chemical formula for antimony(III) oxide.

   _____   1

   (c) In the manufacture of glass, other chemicals can be added to alter the properties of the glass. The element boron can be added to glass to make oven proof dishes.

   (i) Information about an atom of boron is given in the table below.

Particle	Number
proton	5
electron	5
neutron	6

   Use this information to complete the nuclide notation for this atom of boron.

$$\underline{}\mathbf{B}$$

   1

   (ii) Atoms of boron exist which have the same number of protons but a different number of neutrons from that shown in the table.

   What name can be used to describe the different atoms of boron?

   _____   1

   (4)

[Turn over

Marks

2. Rapid inflation of airbags in cars is caused by the production of nitrogen gas.

The graph gives information on the volume of gas produced over 30 microseconds.

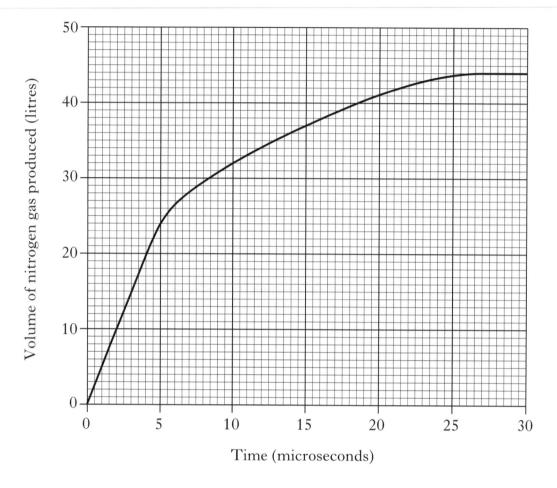

(*a*) (i) Calculate the average rate of reaction between 2 and 10 microseconds.

_____ litres per microsecond   **1**

(ii) At what time has half of the final volume of nitrogen gas been produced?

_____ microseconds   **1**

DO NOT
WRITE
IN THIS
MARGIN

2. **(continued)**

Marks

(b) In some types of airbag, electrical energy causes sodium azide, NaN_3, to decompose producing sodium metal and nitrogen gas.

Write a formula equation for this reaction.

1

(c) Potassium nitrate is also present in the airbag to remove the sodium metal by converting it into sodium oxide.

Why is it necessary to remove the sodium metal?

_____

_____

1

(4)

[Turn over

Marks

3. In the **PPA**, **"Effect of Concentration on Reaction Rate"**, the reaction between sodium persulphate and potassium iodide was investigated.

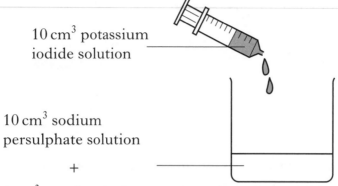

10 cm³ potassium iodide solution

10 cm³ sodium persulphate solution

+

1 cm³ starch solution

The results obtained during this PPA are shown in the table.

Experiment	Volume of sodium persulphate (cm³)	Volume of water (cm³)	Reaction time (s)
1	10	0	126
2	8		162
3	6		210
4	4		336

(a) Complete the results table to show the volumes of water used in experiments 2, 3 and 4.   1

(b) How was the rate of reaction determined?

_____

_____   1

(c) Apart from using a timer, what allowed the accurate measurement of reaction times?

_____

_____   1

(3)

[Turn over for Question 4 on *Page fourteen*

Marks

4. Rhubarb contains oxalic acid, $C_2H_2O_4$.

Oxalic acid reacts with acidified potassium permanganate solution and decolourises it.

The equation for the reaction is:

$$2MnO_4^-(aq) + 5C_2H_2O_4(aq) + 6H^+(aq) \longrightarrow 2Mn^{2+}(aq) + 10CO_2(g) + 8H_2O(\ell)$$

(a) The reaction is catalysed by the $Mn^{2+}(aq)$ ions produced in the reaction.

Using information from the equation, what type of catalyst is $Mn^{2+}(aq)$?

_____   1

(b) A student investigated the effect of surface area on the rate of reaction with acidified potassium permanganate solution.

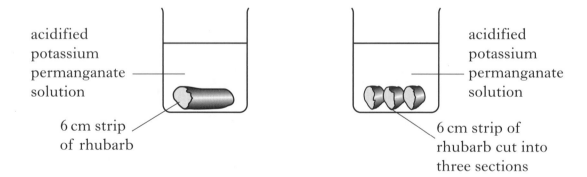

acidified
potassium
permanganate
solution

6 cm strip
of rhubarb

acidified
potassium
permanganate
solution

6 cm strip of
rhubarb cut into
three sections

It was found that when the rhubarb was cut into three sections the reaction was faster. Using collision theory, explain why cutting the rhubarb into three sections increases the rate of reaction.

_____

_____   1

DO NOT WRITE IN THIS MARGIN

4. (continued)

Marks

(*c*) A strip of rhubarb was found to contain 1·8 g of oxalic acid.

How many moles of oxalic acid, $C_2H_2O_4$, are contained in 1·8 g.

(Formula mass of oxalic acid = 90)

____________________ moles **1**

(3)

[Turn over

Marks

5. The alkanals are a homologous series of compounds that all contain the elements carbon, hydrogen and oxygen.

(*a*) What is meant by the term homologous series?

_____

_____   1

(*b*) The combustion of alkanals releases heat energy.

Name of alkanal	Heat energy released when one mole burns (kJ)
methanal	510
ethanal	1056
propanal	1624
butanal	2304

(i) Make a general statement linking the amount of heat energy released and the number of carbon atoms in the alkanal molecules.

_____

_____   1

(ii) Predict the amount of heat energy released, when 1 mole of pentanal burns.

_____ kJ   1

(3)

Marks

6. Kevlar is a polymer which is used in the manufacture of body armour.

(*a*) What property of Kevlar makes it suitable for use in body armour?

_____   1

(*b*) Kevlar is made from the following monomers.

$$\underset{H}{\overset{H}{N}}-\bigcirc-\underset{H}{\overset{H}{N}} \qquad \underset{Cl}{\overset{O}{C}}-\bigcirc-\underset{Cl}{\overset{O}{C}}$$

(i) Draw the structure of the repeating unit formed from these two monomers.

1

(ii) Name the type of link formed.

_____   1

(3)

Marks

7. Ethanol is a member of the alkanol family of compounds.

(a) Ethanol can be manufactured from ethene as shown in the following addition reaction.

$$\begin{array}{ccc} \text{H} & \text{H} & \\ | & | & \\ \text{C} = \text{C} + \text{H}_2\text{O} & \xrightarrow{\text{catalyst}} & \text{H}-\text{C}-\text{C}-\text{H} \\ | & | & \\ \text{H} & \text{H} & \end{array}$$

What other name can be given to this type of addition reaction?

_____   1

(b) Ethanol can be used to make esters which can be used as flavourings for food. The following ester is used to give ice cream a rum flavour.

$$\text{H}-\text{C}-\text{C}-\text{O}-\text{C}-\text{C}-\text{C}-\text{H}$$

Name this ester.

_____   1

(c) Butan-2-ol is another member of the alkanol family.

$$\text{H}-\text{C}-\text{C}-\text{C}-\text{C}-\text{H}$$

Draw the full structural formula for an isomer of butan-2-ol.

1

(3)

DO NOT
WRITE
IN THIS
MARGIN

Marks

8. A student completed the **PPA "Testing for Unsaturation"**. Results from the experiment are shown in the table.

Hydrocarbon	Molecular Formula	Observation with bromine solution	Saturated or unsaturated
A	C_6H_{14}	no change	
B	C_6H_{12}		unsaturated
C	C_6H_{12}		saturated
D	C_6H_{10}	bromine decolourises	

(a) Complete the table. 2

(b) Care had to be taken when using bromine solution. Give a safety precaution, **other** than eye protection, which should be taken when completing this PPA.

_____ 1

(c) Suggest a possible name for hydrocarbon C.

_____ 1

(4)

[Turn over

Marks

9. During digestion, molecules are broken down enabling them to pass through the gut wall. Visking tubing can be used to model the gut wall.

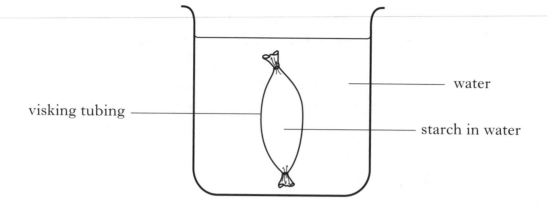

(*a*) Describe how you could use iodine solution to show that starch molecules are too large to pass through the visking tubing.

_____

_____

_____ 1

(*b*) Starch is hydrolysed by the enzyme amylase during digestion.

   (i) What is produced when starch is hydrolysed?

   _____ 1

   (ii) Name another substance which can be used to hydrolyse starch.

   _____ 1

   (3)

Marks

10.

> ### The Dead Zone
>
> In the summer of 2006, a 1000 square mile area of water at the bottom of the Pacific Ocean was found to be covered in dead crabs.
>
> Scientists investigating this found an increased level of chlorophyll at the surface of the ocean and a zero level of oxygen at the bottom of the ocean. The increase in chlorophyll was due to increased numbers of plant plankton.
>
> Scientists think that when plant plankton died they sank to the bottom of the ocean where they were broken down by bacteria during respiration. This used up all the oxygen from the water which resulted in the death of the crabs.
>
> As respiration also produces carbon dioxide, scientists are monitoring the pH of the ocean water.

(a) What is the function of chlorophyll in plant plankton?

_____

_____   1

(b) Why is respiration essential to all living organisms?

_____

_____   1

(c) The pH of ocean water is normally around 8·2.

What effect will the carbon dioxide gas produced during respiration have on the pH of the ocean water?

_____

_____   1

(3)

[Turn over

Marks

11. Egg shells are made up mainly of calcium carbonate. A pupil carried out an experiment to react egg shells with dilute hydrochloric acid. A gas was produced.

(*a*) Complete the diagram to show the apparatus which could have been used to measure the volume of gas produced.

(Additional paper, if required, can be found on *Page twenty-eight*.)

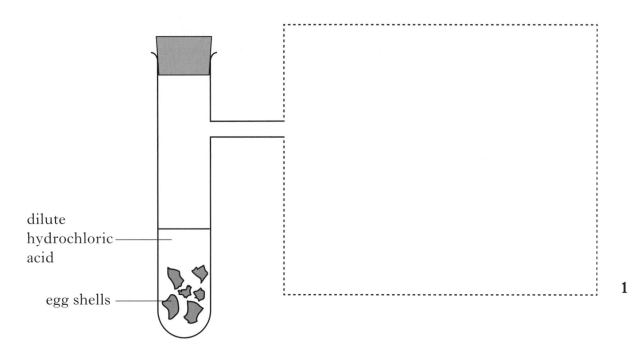

1

(*b*) Name the salt produced in this reaction.

_____

1

(*c*) The volume of gas produced during the reaction was measured.

Time (min)	Volume of gas (cm^3)
0	0
2	47
4	92
6	114
8	118
10	118

11. **(c)** **(continued)**   *Marks*

Plot these results as a line graph.

(Additional graph paper, if required, can be found on *Page twenty-nine*.)

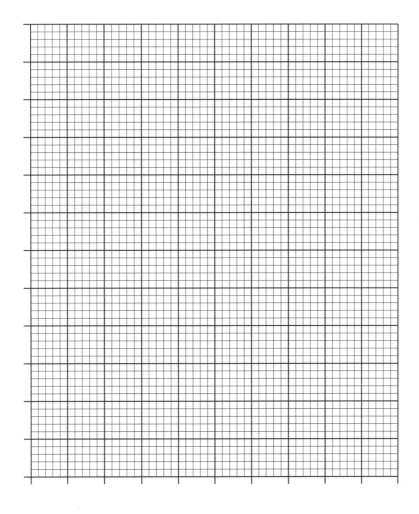

2

(4)

[Turn over

12. Three experiments were carried out to compare the pH and conductivity of weak and strong acids.

Marks

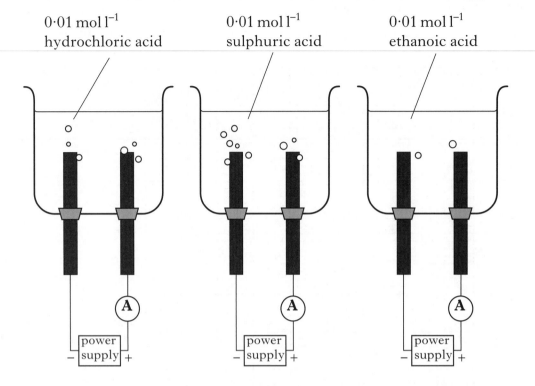

0·01 mol l^{-1} hydrochloric acid 0·01 mol l^{-1} sulphuric acid 0·01 mol l^{-1} ethanoic acid

(*a*) The same gas was produced at the negative electrode in each experiment.

Name the gas that was produced.

_____

1

(*b*) Ethanoic acid is a weak acid.

What is meant by a weak acid?

_____

_____

1

(*c*) Circle the correct words in the table to show how the properties of the sulphuric acid solution compare with the hydrochloric acid solution.

	0·01 mol l^{-1} hydrochloric acid solution	0·01 mol l^{-1} sulphuric acid solution
pH	2	lower the same higher
Current in a conductivity cell (microamps)	45	lower the same higher

1

(3)

Marks

13. A student carried out the following experiment.

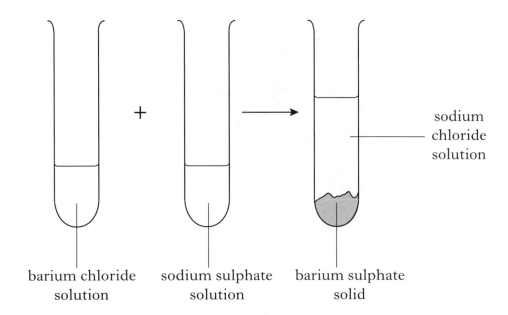

barium chloride   sodium sulphate   barium sulphate
   solution   solution   solid

(a) During the reaction a solid was formed.

Name the type of chemical reaction taking place.

_____   1

(b) The equation for the reaction is

$$Ba^{2+}(aq) + 2Cl^-(aq) + 2Na^+(aq) + SO_4^{2-}(aq) \longrightarrow Ba^{2+}SO_4^{2-}(s) + 2Cl^-(aq) + 2Na^+(aq)$$

(i) Rewrite the equation showing only the ions which react.

1

(ii) What term is used to describe the ions which do not react?

_____   1

(3)

[Turn over

Marks

14. Cutlery can be coated with silver to prevent corrosion and to make it look attractive.

(a) What happens to atoms of a metal during corrosion?

_____

_____   **1**

(b) Electroplating is a process used to coat the cutlery with silver.

This diagram shows how this can be carried out.

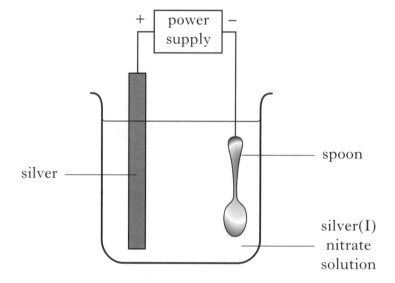

(i) Write the ion-electron equation for the reaction taking place at the positive electrode.

(You may wish to use page 7 of the data booklet to help you.)

_____   **1**

(ii) Why must the cutlery be attached to the **negative** terminal of the power supply?

_____

_____   **1**

(3)

DO NOT
WRITE
IN THIS
MARGIN

15. Rust, iron(III) oxide, that forms on cars can be treated using rust remover which contains phosphoric acid.

Marks

When painted on, rust remover changes iron(III) oxide into iron(III) phosphate.

$$Fe_2O_3 \ + \ 2H_3PO_4 \ \longrightarrow \ 2FePO_4 \ + \ 3H_2O$$

(a) The rust remover contains $250\,cm^3$ of $2\,mol\,l^{-1}$ phosphoric acid.

   (i) Calculate the number of moles of phosphoric acid in the rust remover.

_____ mol   **1**

   (ii) Using your answer in part (i), calculate the mass of iron(III) oxide that will be removed by $250\,cm^3$ of $2\,mol\,l^{-1}$ phosphoric acid.

_____ grams   **2**

(b) The iron(III) phosphate forms an insoluble coating which can be left on to protect the metal from further corrosion.

How does the iron(III) phosphate protect the iron from further corrosion?

_____

_____   **1**

(4)

[END OF QUESTION PAPER]

ADDITIONAL SPACE FOR ANSWERS

ADDITIONAL PAPER FOR QUESTION 11(*a*)

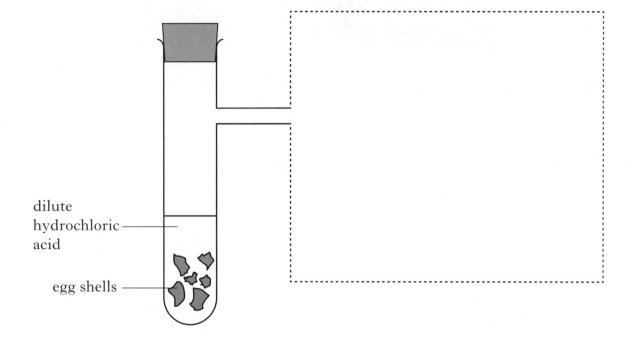

ADDITIONAL SPACE FOR ANSWERS

ADDITIONAL GRAPH PAPER FOR QUESTION 11(*c*)

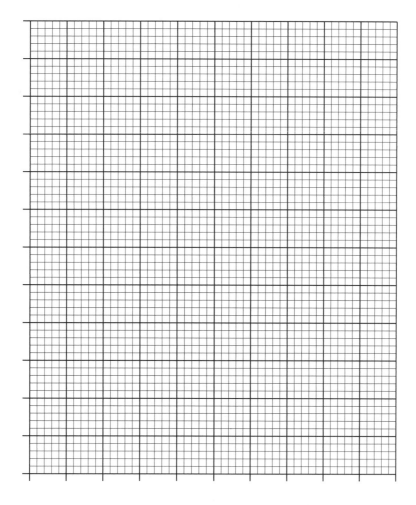

ADDITIONAL SPACE FOR ANSWERS

ADDITIONAL SPACE FOR ANSWERS

[BLANK PAGE]

INTERMEDIATE 2

2013

[BLANK PAGE]

FOR OFFICIAL USE

Section B

Total Marks

X012/11/02

NATIONAL QUALIFICATIONS 2013

FRIDAY, 31 MAY 1.00 PM – 3.00 PM

CHEMISTRY INTERMEDIATE 2

Fill in these boxes and read what is printed below.

Full name of centre

Town

Forename(s)

Surname

Date of birth

Day	Month	Year	Scottish candidate number	Number of seat

Necessary data will be found in the Chemistry Data Booklet for Standard Grade and Intermediate 2.

Section A – Questions 1–30 (30 marks)

Instructions for completion of **Section A** are given on page two.

For this section of the examination you must use an **HB pencil**.

Section B (50 marks)

All questions should be attempted.

The questions may be answered in any order but all answers are to be written in the spaces provided in this answer book, **and must be written clearly and legibly in ink.**

Rough work, if any should be necessary, should be written in this book, and then scored through when the fair copy has been written. If further space is required, a supplementary sheet for rough work may be obtained from the Invigilator.

Additional space for answers will be found at the end of the book. If further space is required, supplementary sheets may be obtained from the Invigilator and should be inserted inside the **front** cover of this booklet.

Before leaving the examination room you must give this book to the Invigilator. If you do not, you may lose all the marks for this paper.

Read carefully

1   Check that the answer sheet provided is for **Chemistry Intermediate 2 (Section A)**.

2   For this section of the examination you must use an **HB pencil** and, where necessary, an eraser.

3   Check that the answer sheet you have been given has **your name**, **date of birth**, **SCN** (Scottish Candidate Number) and **Centre Name** printed on it.

    Do not change any of these details.

4   If any of this information is wrong, tell the Invigilator immediately.

5   If this information is correct, **print** your name and seat number in the boxes provided.

6   The answer to each question is **either** A, B, C or D. Decide what your answer is, then, using your pencil, put a horizontal line in the space provided (see sample question below).

7   There is **only one correct** answer to each question.

8   Any rough working should be done on the question paper or the rough working sheet, **not** on your answer sheet.

9   At the end of the examination, put the **answer sheet for Section A inside the front cover of this answer book**.

Sample Question

To show that the ink in a ball-pen consists of a mixture of dyes, the method of separation would be

    A   chromatography

    B   fractional distillation

    C   fractional crystallisation

    D   filtration.

The correct answer is **A**—chromatography. The answer **A** has been clearly marked in **pencil** with a horizontal line (see below).

Changing an answer

If you decide to change your answer, carefully erase your first answer and using your pencil, fill in the answer you want. The answer below has been changed to **D**.

A   B   C   D

SECTION A

1. In an exothermic reaction

   A   there is no energy change

   B   energy is released to the surroundings

   C   energy is absorbed from the surroundings

   D   the energy of the products is greater than the energy of the reactants.

2. When hydrogen chloride gas is dissolved in water a solution containing hydrogen ions and chloride ions is formed.

   Which equation correctly shows the state symbols for this change?

   A $HCl(g) + H_2O(\ell) \longrightarrow H^+(aq) + Cl^-(aq)$

   B $HCl(\ell) + H_2O(aq) \longrightarrow H^+(\ell) + Cl^-(\ell)$

   C $HCl(aq) + H_2O(\ell) \longrightarrow H^+(aq) + Cl^-(aq)$

   D $HCl(g) + H_2O(\ell) \longrightarrow H^+(\ell) + Cl^-(\ell)$

3. A bottle of whisky contains 40% ethanol by volume.

   Which line in the table is the correct description of the mixture?

	Solute	Solvent	Solution
A	ethanol	whisky	water
B	ethanol	water	whisky
C	water	ethanol	whisky
D	whisky	water	ethanol

4. Many chemical processes involve catalysts.

   Identify the process in which the catalyst could be an enzyme.

   A   Hydration of ethene

   B   Hydrolysis of starch

   C   Cracking of hydrocarbons

   D   Formation of alkenes from alkanes

5. Which line in the table correctly describes a proton?

	Mass	Charge	Location
A	negligible	0	outside nucleus
B	negligible	−1	outside nucleus
C	1	+1	in nucleus
D	1	0	in nucleus

6. In a hydrogen fluoride molecule, the atoms share electrons in order to achieve the same electron arrangements as atoms in group

   A   0

   B   1

   C   2

   D   7.

7. What is the name of the compound with the formula VO_2?

   A   Vanadium(V) oxide

   B   Vanadium(IV) oxide

   C   Vanadium(III) oxide

   D   Vanadium(II) oxide

8. $4NH_3 + xO_2 \rightarrow 4NO + yH_2O$

   The equation will be balanced when

   A $x = 5, y = 6$

   B $x = 5, y = 10$

   C $x = 3, y = 6$

   D $x = 3, y = 10$.

9. Which of the following substances has the smallest gram formula mass?

   A CO

   B CO_2

   C N_2

   D CH_4

10.

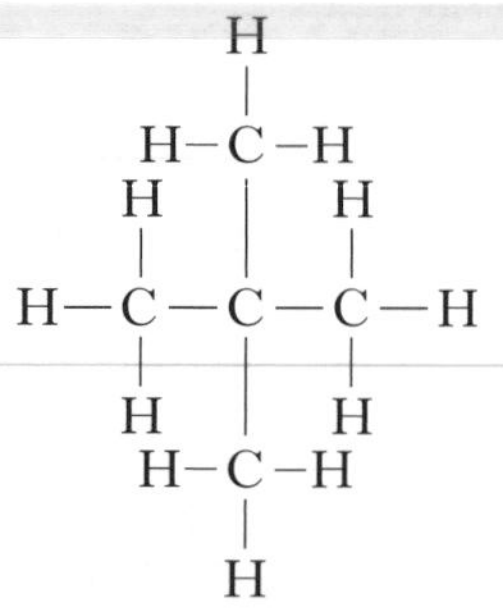

$$
\begin{array}{c}
\text{H} \\
| \\
\text{H}-\text{C}-\text{H} \\
\quad\text{H} \;\;|\;\; \text{H} \\
\;\;|\quad|\quad| \\
\text{H}-\text{C}-\text{C}-\text{C}-\text{H} \\
\;\;|\quad|\quad| \\
\quad\text{H} \;\;|\;\; \text{H} \\
\text{H}-\text{C}-\text{H} \\
| \\
\text{H}
\end{array}
$$

Which of the following compounds is an isomer of the one shown above?

A

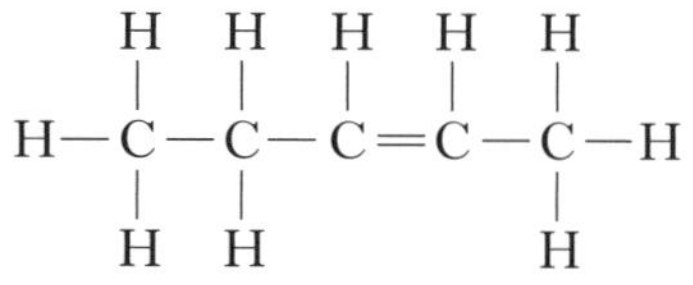

$$
\begin{array}{c}
\;\;\text{H}\;\;\text{H}\;\;\text{H}\;\;\text{H}\;\;\text{H} \\
\;\;|\quad|\quad|\quad|\quad| \\
\text{H}-\text{C}-\text{C}-\text{C}=\text{C}-\text{C}-\text{H} \\
\;\;|\quad|\qquad\quad| \\
\;\;\text{H}\;\;\text{H}\qquad\quad\text{H}
\end{array}
$$

B

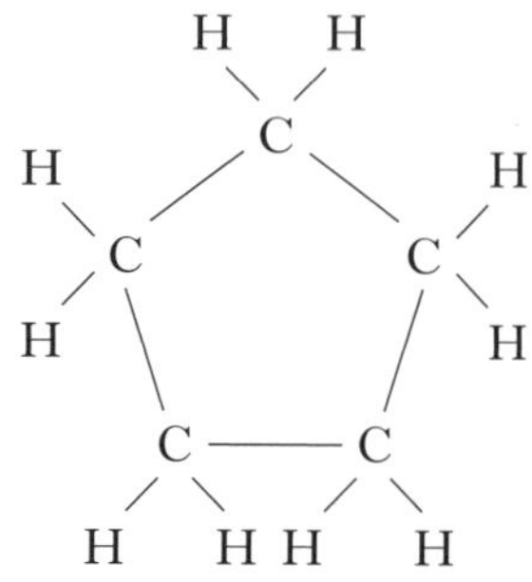

C

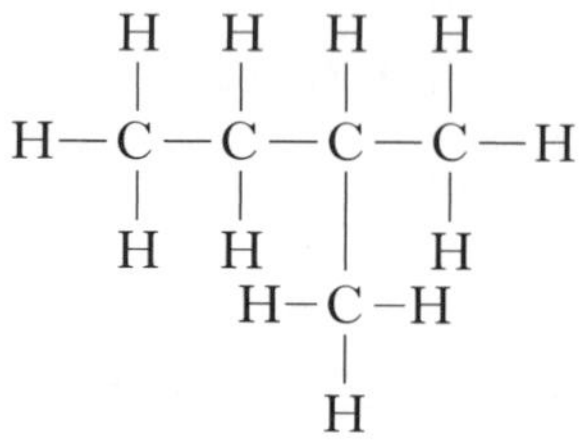

$$
\begin{array}{c}
\;\;\text{H}\;\;\text{H}\;\;\text{H}\;\;\text{H} \\
\;\;|\quad|\quad|\quad| \\
\text{H}-\text{C}-\text{C}-\text{C}-\text{C}-\text{H} \\
\;\;|\quad|\quad|\quad| \\
\;\;\text{H}\;\;\text{H}\;\;|\;\;\text{H} \\
\qquad\quad\text{H}-\text{C}-\text{H} \\
\qquad\qquad| \\
\qquad\qquad\text{H}
\end{array}
$$

D

$$
\begin{array}{c}
\qquad\text{H} \\
\qquad| \\
\qquad\text{H}-\text{C}-\text{H} \\
\;\;\text{H}\;\;\text{H}\;\;|\;\;\text{H} \\
\;\;|\quad|\quad|\quad| \\
\text{H}-\text{C}-\text{C}-\text{C}-\text{C}-\text{H} \\
\;\;|\quad|\quad|\quad| \\
\;\;\text{H}\;\;\text{H}\;\;|\;\;\text{H} \\
\qquad\text{H}-\text{C}-\text{H} \\
\qquad\qquad| \\
\qquad\qquad\text{H}
\end{array}
$$

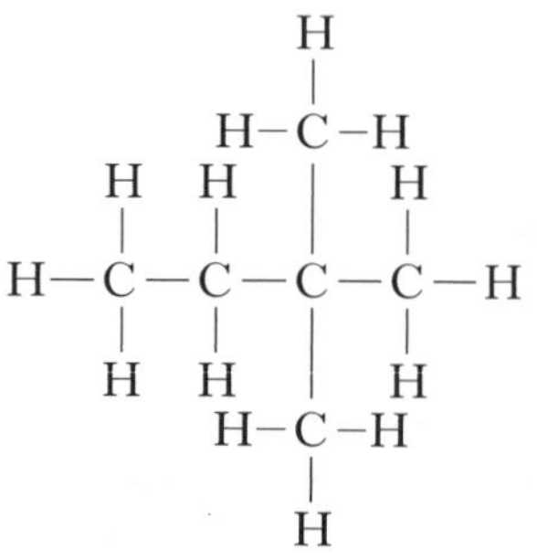

11. When a compound is burned completely, the products are carbon dioxide and water.

From this information, it can be concluded that the compound must contain

A   carbon only

B   hydrogen only

C   carbon and hydrogen

D   carbon, hydrogen and oxygen.

12. Which of the following hydrocarbons could be cyclohexane?

Hydrocarbon	Molecular formula	Observations on adding bromine solution
A	C_6H_{14}	no colour change
B	C_6H_{12}	rapid decolourisation
C	C_6H_{12}	no colour change
D	C_6H_{10}	rapid decolourisation

13. Ethanol can be produced from sugar cane by

A   oxidation

B   fermentation

C   polymerisation

D   catalytic hydration.

14. Propan-1-ol can be dehydrated.

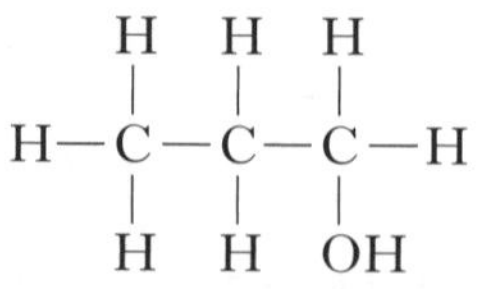

$$
\begin{array}{c}
\;\;\text{H}\;\;\text{H}\;\;\text{H} \\
\;\;|\quad|\quad| \\
\text{H}-\text{C}-\text{C}-\text{C}-\text{H} \\
\;\;|\quad|\quad| \\
\;\;\text{H}\;\;\text{H}\;\;\text{OH}
\end{array}
$$

Which of the following compounds is a product of the reaction?

A   Propanoic acid

B   Propyl propanoate

C   Propene

D   Propane

15. The first four members of the amine homologous series are:

What is the general formula for this homologous series?

A $C_n H_{n+4} N$

B $C_n H_{2n+3} N$

C $C_n H_{3n+2} N$

D $C_n H_{4n+1} N$

16. Biopol is a polymer which is

A   natural and biodegradeable

B   synthetic and biodegradeable

C   natural and non-biodegradeable

D   synthetic and non-biodegradeable.

17. Which of the following fatty acids contains the most double bonds per molecule?

A $C_{17}H_{35}COOH$

B $C_{17}H_{33}COOH$

C $C_{17}H_{31}COOH$

D $C_{17}H_{29}COOH$

18. An alkaline solution contains

A   hydroxide ions but no hydrogen ions

B   equal numbers of hydrogen and hydroxide ions

C   more hydroxide ions than hydrogen ions

D   more hydrogen ions than hydroxide ions.

19. In which of the following experiments would both carbohydrates give an orange precipitate when heated with Benedict's solution?

A

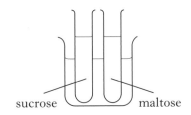

sucrose   maltose

B

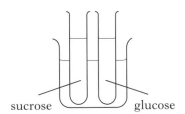

sucrose   glucose

C

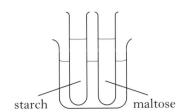

starch   maltose

D

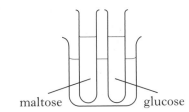

maltose   glucose

20. When hydrochloric acid with a pH of 3 is diluted with water to give a solution with a pH of 6, the concentration of

   A $H^+(aq)$ ions decreases

   B $OH^-(aq)$ ions decreases

   C $H^+(aq)$ ions and the concentration of $OH^-(aq)$ ions become equal

   D $H^+(aq)$ ions and the concentration of $OH^-(aq)$ ions remain unchanged.

21. 0·25 mol of potassium hydroxide was dissolved in water and the solution made up to 500 cm³.

   What was the concentration, in mol l⁻¹, of the solution which was formed?

   A   0·0005

   B   0·125

   C   0·5

   D   2·0

22. Which of the following compounds is a base?

   A   Sodium carbonate

   B   Sodium chloride

   C   Sodium nitrate

   D   Sodium sulphate

23. Which of the following gases reacts with an alkaline solution?

   A   Argon

   B   Oxygen

   C   Ammonia

   D   Nitrogen dioxide

24. Which of the following compounds is a salt?

   A   Ammonium chloride

   B   Calcium oxide

   C   Hydrogen chloride

   D   Sodium hydroxide

25. When nickel(II) chloride solution is added to sodium carbonate solution an insoluble solid is formed.

   A sample of the solid can be separated from the mixture by

   A   condensation

   B   distillation

   C   evaporation

   D   filtration.

26.

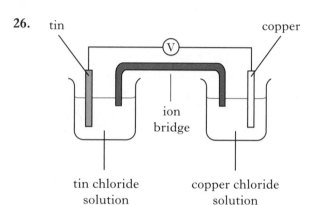

   In the cell shown electrons flow through

   A   the solution from copper to tin

   B   the solution from tin to copper

   C   the wires from copper to tin

   D   the wires from tin to copper.

27.

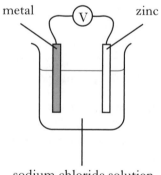

sodium chloride solution

   Which of the following metals, when linked to zinc, would give the highest cell voltage?

   (You may wish to use the data booklet to help you.)

   A   Copper

   B   Iron

   C   Magnesium

   D   Tin

28. In which test tube will the iron nail corrode fastest?

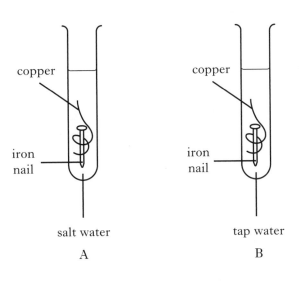

salt water
A

tap water
B

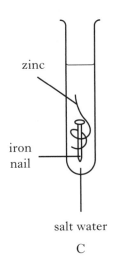

salt water
C

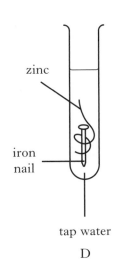

tap water
D

29. When a metal element reacts to form a compound the metal is

   A   displaced

   B   oxidised

   C   precipitated

   D   reduced.

30. Which of the following metals can be obtained from its ore by heating with carbon monoxide?

(You may wish to use the data booklet to help you.)

   A   Aluminium

   B   Calcium

   C   Magnesium

   D   Nickel

Candidates are reminded that the answer sheet for Section A MUST be placed INSIDE the front cover of this answer book.

[Turn over

[BLANK PAGE]

Marks

SECTION B

50 marks are available in this section of the paper.

All answers must be written clearly and legibly in ink.

1. (*a*) Strontium compounds have many uses.

   (i) Strontium nitrate is used in warning flares.

   What colour of flame will strontium nitrate give?

   (You may wish to use the data booklet to help you.)

   _____   1

   (ii) Strontium chloride hexahydrate can be used in toothpaste for sensitive teeth as it plugs the holes in the tooth enamel.

   This is possible because strontium has similar chemical properties to calcium.

   Why does strontium have similar chemical properties to calcium?

   _____   1

   (*b*) Strontium can be extracted from the compound strontium chloride using electrolysis.

   Label the diagram to show the **charge** on each electrode.

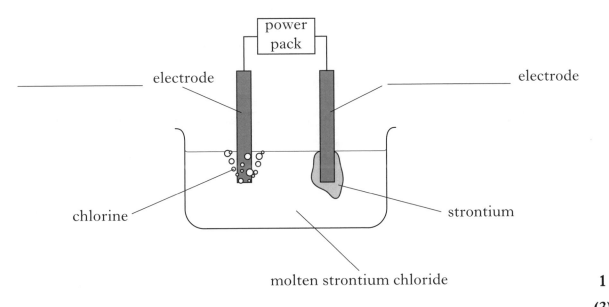

1

(3)

[Turn over

Marks

2. In the **PPA**, "**Effect of temperature on reaction rate**", the reaction between sodium thiosulphate solution and dilute hydrochloric acid is investigated.

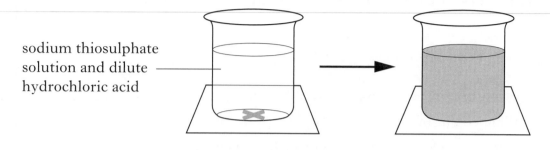

sodium thiosulphate solution and dilute hydrochloric acid

(a) How is the rate of the reaction determined?

_____

_____   1

(b) State a factor which should be kept constant.

_____

_____   1

(c) Apart from wearing safety glasses, state another safety precaution which must be taken when carrying out this experiment.

_____

_____   1

(d) The equation for the reaction taking place is

$$2Na^+(aq) + S_2O_3^{2-}(aq) + 2H^+(aq) + 2Cl^-(aq) \longrightarrow 2Na^+(aq) + 2Cl^-(aq) + SO_2(g) + S(s) + H_2O(\ell)$$

Circle a spectator ion in the equation.   1

(4)

[Turn over for Question 3 on *Page twelve*

Marks

3. Magnesium reacts with dilute sulphuric acid to produce a gas.

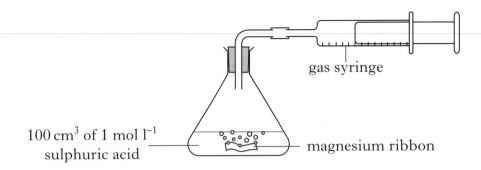

100 cm³ of 1 mol l⁻¹
sulphuric acid — magnesium ribbon

(a) Name the gas produced in this reaction.

_____   1

(b) A student carried out the experiment. A graph of the results was plotted.

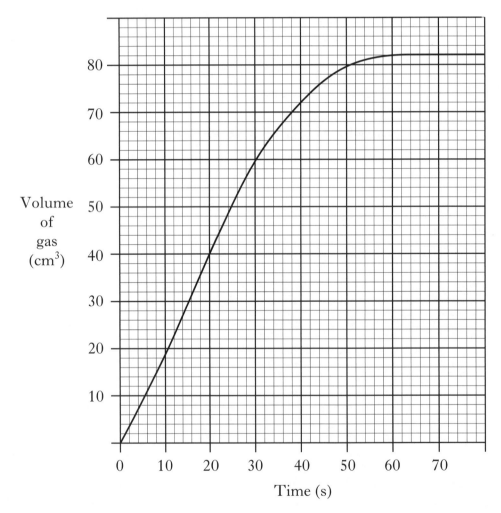

Calculate the average rate of the reaction, in cm³ s⁻¹, for the first 40 seconds.

_____ cm³ s⁻¹   1

Marks

3. (continued)

(c) Predict the total volume of gas produced if the experiment was repeated using silver.

_____ cm^3.

1

(d) The student repeated the experiment using $100 \, cm^3$ of $1 \, mol \, l^{-1}$ ethanoic acid solution and the same mass of magnesium ribbon.

How would this affect the rate of the reaction?

_____

1

(4)

[Turn over

Marks

4. Tritium is a naturally occurring isotope of hydrogen. It can be represented as

$$_{1}^{3}\text{H}$$

(a) Complete the table to show the number of particles in an atom of tritium.

Type of particle	Number of particles
proton	
neutron	
electron	

1

(b) Hydrogen has three isotopes.

Isotope of hydrogen	Mass number
protium	1
deuterium	2
tritium	3

The relative atomic mass of hydrogen is 1.

Which isotope of hydrogen is the most abundant?

_____

1

(2)

Marks

5. Electronegativity is a measure of the attraction that an atom has for the bonded electrons.

    (*a*) What type of bond is formed when the attraction of the atoms for the bonded electrons is different?

      _____   1

    (*b*) The chart shows the electronegativity values for some elements in the Periodic Table.

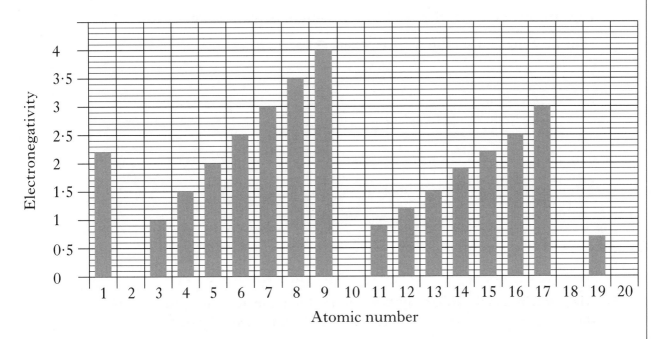

      (i) Describe what happens to the electronegativity values going across a period in the Periodic Table.

         _____

         _____   1

      (ii) Draw a bar on the chart to show the electronegativity value for the element calcium, atomic number 20.   1

                                                (3)

[Turn over

Marks

6. Dishwasher tablets contain many different types of chemicals.

(a) A dishwasher tablet was found to contain 1·57 g of the bleaching agent, sodium percarbonate.

How many moles are there in 1·57g of sodium percarbonate?

(Formula mass of sodium percarbonate = 157.)

_____ moles   **1**

(b) Many dishwasher tablets contain sand which can help to remove food deposits. Sand contains the covalent compound silicon dioxide.

What type of **structure** does silicon dioxide have?

(You may wish to use page 6 of the data booklet to help you.)

_____   **1**

(c) Phosphate ions, present in some types of dishwasher tablets, react with calcium ions in water forming calcium phosphate.

Write the formula for calcium phosphate.

_____   **1**

(3)

Marks

7. The car industry and the Government have taken a number of steps to reduce the emissions of pollutant gases from cars.

(a) Catalytic converters reduce the emission of carbon monoxide by converting it to a harmless gas.

Name this harmless gas.

_____ **1**

(b) Car tax is based on the mass of carbon dioxide gas produced per kilometre travelled by a car.

(i) The volume of carbon dioxide produced by a car is measured and then converted into mass using the following equation.

$$\text{Mass of carbon dioxide gas (g)} = \frac{100 \times \text{volume of carbon dioxide gas (l)}}{56 \cdot 3}$$

Calculate the mass of carbon dioxide gas which is produced by a car emitting 70·4 l of carbon dioxide gas.

_____ g **1**

(ii) Information about car tax bands is shown in the tables.

Car tax band	Mass of carbon dioxide gas emitted per kilometre (g)
A	Up to 100
B	101–110
C	111–120
D	121–130
E	131–140
F	141–150
G	151–165

Car tax band	12 month rate (£)
A	0·00
B	20·00
C	30·00
D	95·00
E	115·00
F	130·00
G	165·00

What would it cost to tax a car, for 12 months, which emits 146 g of carbon dioxide per kilometre travelled?

£ _____ **1**

(3)

Marks

8. Crude oil is a mixture of hydrocarbons which can be separated into fractions by fractional distillation.

Fraction	Number of Carbon atoms
Refinery gas	1–5
Petrol	5–10
Paraffin	10–16
Diesel	14–20
Lubricating oil	20–50
Bitumen	50 or more

Crude oil →

(a) What property of hydrocarbons is used to separate crude oil into fractions?

_____

_____   1

(b) The viscosity of four fractions was compared by measuring the rate of fall of a ball bearing. The diagram shows the position of the ball bearings 10 seconds after being dropped.

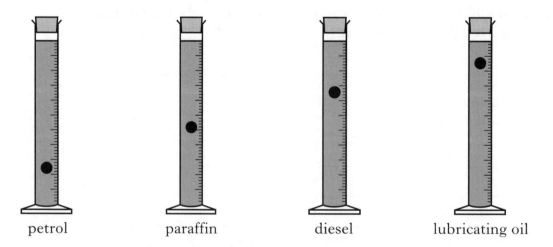

petrol   paraffin   diesel   lubricating oil

What effect does the number of carbon atoms have on the viscosity of a fraction?

_____

_____   1

DO NOT WRITE IN THIS MARGIN

Marks

8. (continued)

(*c*) Petrol contains the following molecule.

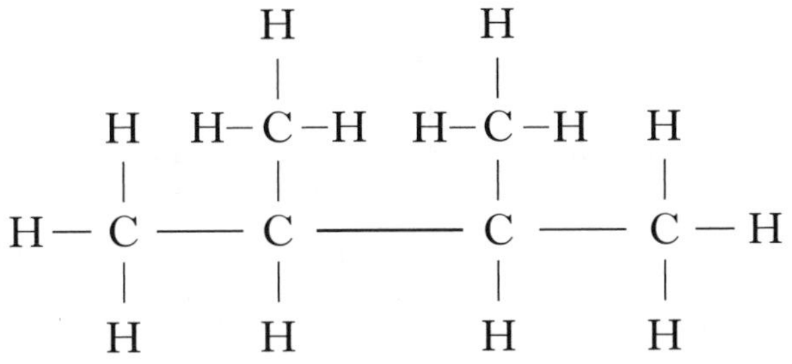

Name this molecule.

______________________________ **1**

(3)

[Turn over

Marks

9. Alkenes can undergo different reactions.

(*a*) In ozonolysis an alkene reacts with ozone forming two molecules. The ozonolysis of hex-3-ene is shown.

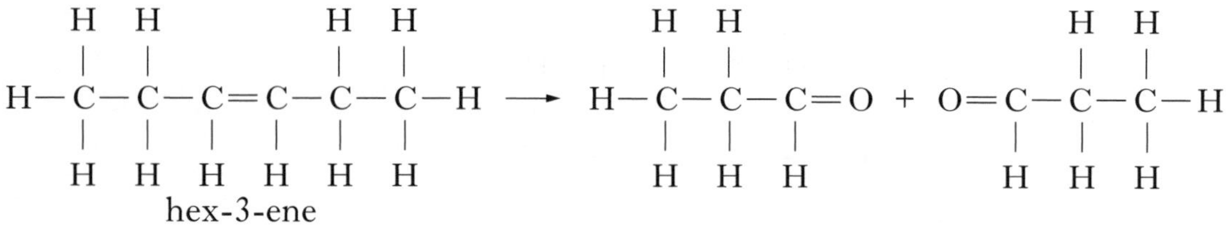

hex-3-ene

Draw the products formed by the ozonolysis of hex-2-ene.

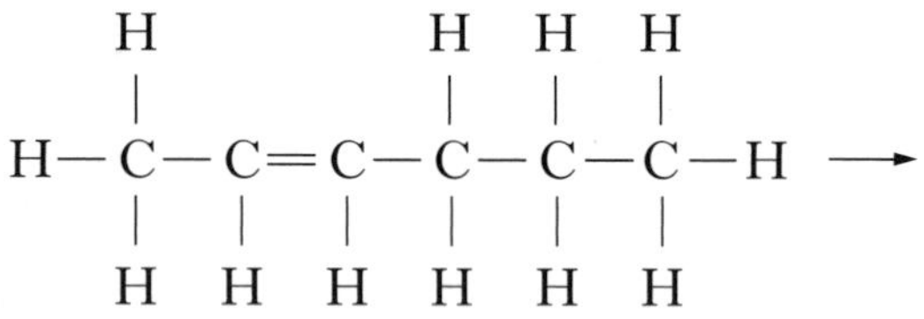

1

(*b*) Potassium permanganate can be used to convert alkenes into two molecules.

The conversion of pent-1-ene is shown.

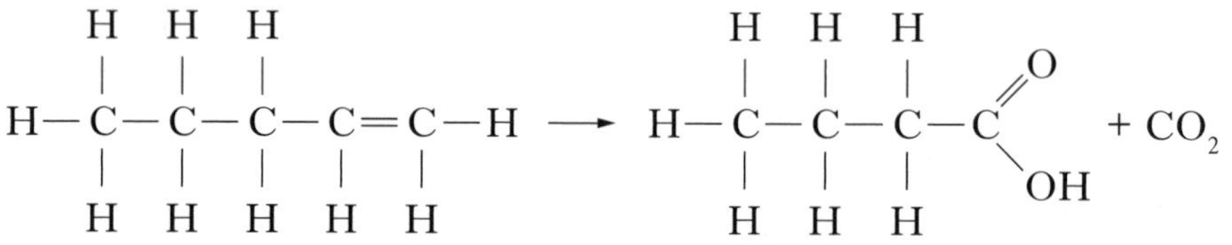

molecule X

(i) Name molecule X.

____ **1**

(ii) State the test for carbon dioxide.

____ **1**

(3)

Marks

10. Some waterproof clothing contains a thin layer of the plastic PTFE.

(a) PTFE is heated and reshaped to make thin layers.

What term is used to describe a plastic which can be heated and reshaped?

_____ 1

(b) (i) PTFE is a polymer made from the monomer shown.

$$\begin{array}{ccc} F & & F \\ | & & | \\ C & = & C \\ | & & | \\ F & & F \end{array}$$

Draw a section of the PTFE polymer, showing three monomer units joined together.

1

(ii) Name this type of polymerisation reaction.

_____ 1

(c) Name a toxic gas produced when PTFE is burned.

_____ 1

(4)

Marks

11.

Migraine, a type of headache, is caused when calcium ions promote the release of a chemical called CGRP in the nervous tissues. Scientists are using cone snails to develop a treatment for migraine. Cone snails produce a chemical which can be used to prevent the release of CGRP.

(a) What is the electron arrangement for a calcium ion, Ca^{2+}?

_____ 1

(b) CGRP is formed from different amino acids.

A short sequence of CGRP is shown.

(i) Circle a peptide link in the above section.   1

(ii) Draw **one** of the amino acids used to form the above section.

1

(3)

Marks

12. Fats and oils are examples of esters. The structure of the fat glyceryl tristearate is shown below.

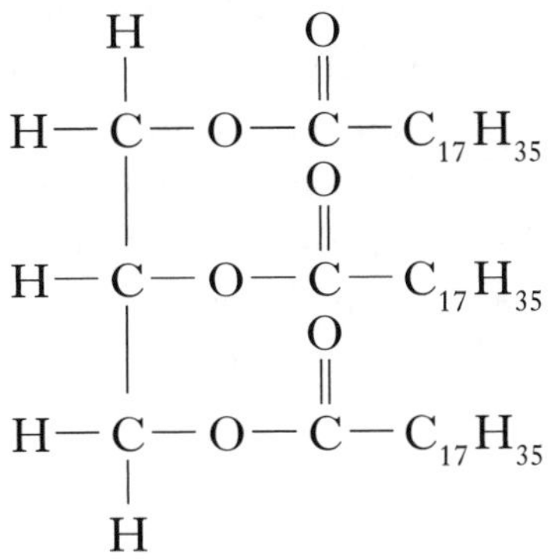

$$
\begin{array}{c}
\text{H} \qquad\quad \text{O} \\
| \qquad\qquad \| \\
\text{H}-\text{C}-\text{O}-\text{C}-\text{C}_{17}\text{H}_{35} \\
| \qquad\qquad \text{O} \\
\qquad\qquad\quad \| \\
\text{H}-\text{C}-\text{O}-\text{C}-\text{C}_{17}\text{H}_{35} \\
| \qquad\qquad \text{O} \\
\qquad\qquad\quad \| \\
\text{H}-\text{C}-\text{O}-\text{C}-\text{C}_{17}\text{H}_{35} \\
| \\
\text{H}
\end{array}
$$

(a) Draw an ester group.

1

(b) Fats and oils can be broken down to form glycerol and fatty acids.

Name this type of chemical reaction.

_____ 1

(c) The equation below shows the breakdown of glyceryl tristearate to form glycerol and stearic acid.

$$C_{57}H_{110}O_6 \quad + \quad 3H_2O \longrightarrow C_3H_8O_3 \quad + \quad 3C_{18}H_{36}O_2$$

glyceryl tristearate   water   glycerol   stearic acid

GFM = 890 g

Calculate the mass of stearic acid produced from 8·9 g of glyceryl tristearate.

_____ g   2

(4)

Marks

13.

When a hippopotamus is seen out of water it looks as though it is bleeding. This is due to a red coloured secretion which protects the hippopotamus against sunburn caused by UVB radiation. Scientists have found that one of the active ingredients in this natural sunscreen is a chemical called hipposudoric acid.

hipposudoric acid

(a) (i) Suggest a pH value for hipposudoric acid.

_____   1

(ii) Hipposudoric acid contains a hydroxyl group.

Circle the hydroxyl group in the structure of hipposudoric acid.   1

Marks

13. (continued)

(*b*) Bottles of sun cream display a sun protection factor which gives an indication of how well the sun cream protects against UVB radiation.

The table gives information about sun protection factors.

Sun protection factor	0	2	4	8	15	30	50
UVB radiation screened (%)	0	50	70	88	94	97	98

Draw a line graph to show the percentage of UVB radiation screened by different sun protection factors.

(Additional graph paper, if required, can be found on *Page twenty-eight*.)

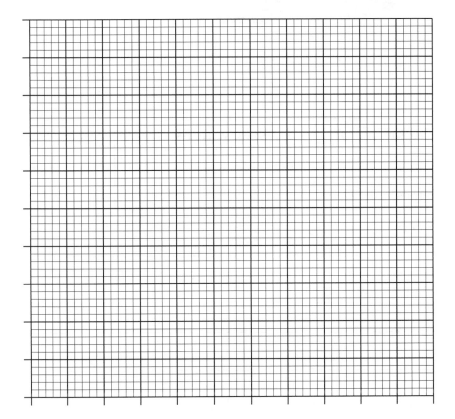

2

(4)

[Turn over

Marks

14. A student's report is shown for the **PPA "Reaction of metals with oxygen"**.

Title   Reactions of Metals with Oxygen   **Date** 15/11/12

Aim

Procedure   The apparatus required to carry out the experiment was collected and assembled as shown.

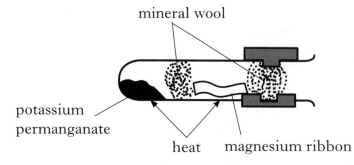

potassium permanganate

mineral wool

heat   magnesium ribbon

Results

Metal	Observations
zinc	moderately fast reaction
magnesium	
copper	

(a) State the aim of the experiment.

_____

_____   1

(b) Why is potassium permanganate used in this experiment?

_____

_____   1

(c) Complete the table to show the observations for magnesium and copper.   1

(d) For safety reasons this experiment would not be carried out with potassium metal.

Suggest a reason for this.

_____   1

(4)

Marks

15. Titanium metal is used to make dental braces.

Titanium is extracted from its ore in the Kroll process. One step in this process involves the displacement of titanium chloride by sodium metal.

The equation is shown.

$$4Na \quad + \quad TiCl_4 \quad \longrightarrow \quad 4NaCl \quad + \quad Ti$$

(*a*) What does this method of extraction tell you about the reactivity of titanium metal compared to sodium metal?

_____   **1**

(*b*) During the displacement, sodium atoms, Na, form sodium ions, Na^+.

Write the ion-electron equation for this change.

   1

(*c*) The displacement reaction is carried out in an atmosphere of the noble gas, argon.

Suggest why an argon atmosphere is used.

_____

_____   **1**

   (3)

[END OF QUESTION PAPER]

ADDITIONAL SPACE FOR ANSWERS

ADDITIONAL PAPER FOR QUESTION 13(*b*)

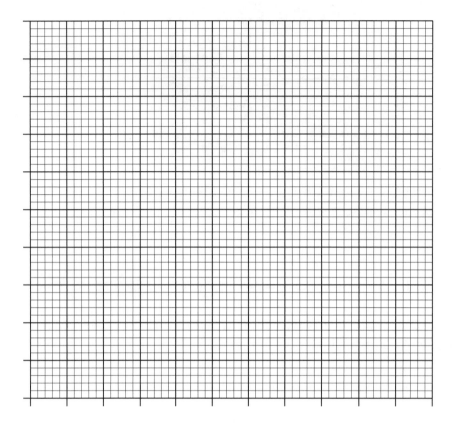

ADDITIONAL SPACE FOR ANSWERS

ADDITIONAL SPACE FOR ANSWERS

DO NOT
WRITE
IN THIS
MARGIN

ADDITIONAL SPACE FOR ANSWERS

Acknowledgements

Permission has been sought from all relevant copyright holders and Hodder Gibson is grateful for the use of the following:

An extract adapted from 'Autumn days' by Victoria Ashton. Taken from 'Education in Chemistry', Vol 38, No 5, September 2001 © Royal Society of Chemistry (2010 page 18);

Image © J Reineke/Shutterstock.com (2013 page 24);

Image © Olga Miltsova/Shutterstock.com (2013 page 27).

INTERMEDIATE 2 | ANSWER SECTION

SQA INTERMEDIATE 2
CHEMISTRY 2009–2013

CHEMISTRY INTERMEDIATE 2
2009

SECTION A

1.	A	11.	A	21.	D
2.	C	12.	B	22.	B
3.	D	13.	C	23.	A
4.	B	14.	D	24.	D
5.	B	15.	C	25.	C
6.	A	16.	A	26.	C
7.	D	17.	D	27.	A
8.	C	18.	A	28.	C
9.	B	19.	D	29.	A
10.	D	20.	A	30.	B

SECTION B

1. (a) 11
      13

   (b) (i)

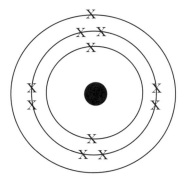

   (ii) The attraction/pull/electrostatic force to the positively charged nucleus (and the (negatively charged) electrons)
   Attraction/pull/electrostatic force between (positive) protons

2. (a) Potassium permanganate
      Water
      (Conc.) Sulphuric acid

   (b) (i) As the atomic number increases the melting point increases

   (ii) 470°C ± 20

3. (a) Exothermic

   (b) (i) Both labels + units
         Both scales
         Plotting points
         Joining points

   (ii) 13 g

   (c) Reduces heat loss from beaker to the surroundings

4. (a) Fe_2O_3 (s) + $\underline{3}CO$(g) ⟶ $\underline{2}Fe$ (l) + $\underline{3}$ CO_2 (g)

   (b) CO_2 (g) + C (s) ⟶ 2 CO (g)
         1 mole ⟶ 2 moles
         12 g ⟶ 56 g
         1200 kg ⟶ 5600 kg

   (c) To provide oxygen (for the reaction which takes place in zone 1)
      To make CO_2
      For complete combustion

5. (a) (As gases have) different boiling points
      Different boiling or melting points

   (b) liquid

   (c) Neutralisation

6. (a) A substance that is burned/combusts to produce energy/heat

   (b) (i) Above zero → 35

   (ii) The smaller the number of carbons in the molecule, the more efficient/useful/better (the fuel)

7. (a) Aluminium oxide (Al_2O_3)

   (b) (i) Butene/C_4H_8

   (ii) (Bromine solution would) decolourise/change from brown to colourless

8. (a) Ethyne/etyne

   (b) (i)

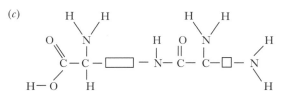

   (ii) Bromines are not attached to adjacent carbon atoms

9. (a)

   —N
      ⟨ H
      ⟨ H

   (b) Amino acids

   (c)

10. (a) Starch + water → glucose

   (b) Fermentation
      Anaerobic respiration

   (c)

      CH_3COOH

   (d) Methyl ethanoate

11. (a) Biological catalyst

   (b) (i) One which does not completely/partially ionise/dissociate (into ions)

   (ii) Titration
      Volumetric titration

12. (a) 167 (s)

   (b) (Increasing the number of rhubarb cubes) increases the surface area /concentration/ more particles

(c) (i) $\dfrac{100}{1000} \times = 0.1$ moles

    (ii) 0.1 moles reacts with $5/2 \times 0.1 = 0.25$ moles

13. (a) ...until no more solid reacts/until it no longer reacts

    (b) To ensure that all of the acid is reacted

    (c) $+ CO_2 (g) + H_2O (l)$

14. (a) Fe_2O_3

    (b) $Fe^{2+} (aq) \rightarrow Fe^{3+} (aq) + e^-$

    (c) Iron loses electrons to (less reactive) lead

15. (a) $2OH^- (aq) + 2H^+ (aq) \quad\rightarrow\quad 2 H_2O (l)$

    (b) (i) Barium hydroxide solution contains a higher concentration of hydroxide ions

       (ii) There are no free ions in

CHEMISTRY INTERMEDIATE 2
2010

SECTION A

1.	A	11.	A	21.	C
2.	D	12.	D	22.	D
3.	C	13.	B	23.	A
4.	D	14.	D	24.	A
5.	C	15.	B	25.	C
6.	D	16.	C	26.	A
7.	B	17.	A	27.	B
8.	B	18.	A	28.	A
9.	C	19.	B	29.	D
10.	A	20.	C	30.	C

SECTION B

1. (a) Nucleus/nuclei

    (b) (i) 8
       (ii) Same/equal number of (positive) protons as (negative) electrons

          or

          Positive charge of protons cancels negative charge of electrons

          or

          Protons cancel out electrons
       (iii) Alkali metals

2. (a) Endothermic

    (b) *All three required:*
       (s) and (1) and (aq)

    (c) Solvent

    (d) $\dfrac{6.72}{0.2 \times 4.2}$

       $= 8$

3. (a) Covalent ($\frac{1}{2}$ mark)
       Network ($\frac{1}{2}$ mark)

    (b) (i)

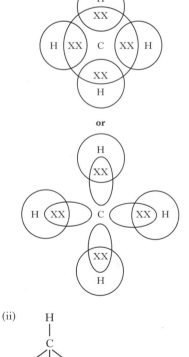

       (ii)

4. (a) (i) 25(%)
    (ii) $25/100 \times 6 = 1.5$

  (b) 4 moles to 2 moles
    $4 \times 108g = 2 \times 248$
        $432 = 496$
    $1.08 = 1.08 \times 496/432$
        $= 1.24$
    or
    no of moles of Ag   = $1.08/108$
                    = 0.01 moles
    no of moles of Ag_2S = $0.01/2$
                    = 0.005
    GFM Ag_2S = 248
    Mass of Ag_2S = 0.005×248
                   = 1.24

5. (a) Heat the catalyst first and then the liquid paraffin/ mineral wool

  (b) To prevent suck-back

  (c) (i) Aluminium oxide/Al_2O_3/(Aluminium) silicate
    (ii) Allows reaction to occur at lower temperature/
       Lower energy required/
       Lower activation energy

  (d) Addition

6. (a)

```
    H   H   O   H   H   H
    |   |   ‖   |   |   |
H — C — C — C — C — C — C — H
    |   |       |   |   |
    H   H       H   H   H
```

  (b) Heptan-4-one

  (c) 147 – 155

7. (a) (i) Fermentation/
       Anaerobic respiration
    (ii) Enzyme/biological catalyst

  (b) Yeast is denatured/destroyed/loses its shape
    Enzyme is denatured/destroyed/loses its shape

  (c) Distillation
    Correct description of the distillation process should include both boiling and condensation stages

8. (a) Esters

  (b) (i) Hydrolysis
    (ii)

```
    H   H   H       O
    |   |   |      ⫽
H — C — C — C — C
    |   |   |      \
    H   H   H       OH
```

9. (a) Photosynthesis

  (b) Glucose turns Benedict's (solution) from blue to (brick) red/yellow/orange/green
    or
    Iodine turns blue/black/purple with starch

  (c) Circle /underline any of the – OH groups

  (d) 2,8

10. (a) Any value below 7

  (b) (i) As the temperature increases the solubility decreases
      or
      As the temperature decreases the solubility increases
    (ii) 1.90-1.94

11. (a) Acid rain/
    Dissolved/absorbed SO_2
    Dissolved/absorbed NO_2/oxides of nitrogen/
    Dissolved/absorbed CO_2
    Dissolved/absorbed soluble non metal oxides

  (b) (i) *All three required:*
      Calcium, carbon, oxygen
      $Ca/C/O/O_2$
    (ii) Water/H_2O
      or hydrogen/H_2

12. (a) Stops air/oxygen **or** water/moisture
    Physical barrier to air/oxygen **or** water/moisture
    Stops iron losing electrons to oxygen **and** water

  (b) (i) Galvanising
    (ii) Zinc sacrifices itself
      Zinc is being oxidised
      Zinc corrodes (by losing electrons)

      The zinc gives away its electrons (to the iron)
      Zinc is more reactive
      Zinc is higher up in the ECS

13. (a) The reading on the pH probe shows 7/neutral

  (b) Moles of acid = $C \times V$
                = 0.1×0.02
                = 0.002
    1 mole to 2 moles
    moles of NaOH = $0.002 \times 2 = 0.004$
    c = n/v
      = $0.004/0.05$
      = 0.08
    or
    $H \times C \times V = OH \times C \times V$
    $2 \times 0.1 \times 20 = 1 \times C \times 50$
              $4 = 50C$
    $C = 4/50$
      $= 0.08$
    or
    $$\frac{C_A V_A}{C_B V_B} = \frac{b}{a}$$
    $$\frac{0.1 \times 20}{C_B \times 50} = \frac{1}{2}$$
    $$C_B = \frac{0.1 \times 20 \times 2}{50}$$
         $$= \frac{4}{50}$$
         $= 0.08$

14. (a) (i) *All three required:*
      LHS = copper/Cu
      Top RHS = Iron/Fe
      Bottom RHS = $100cm^3$ 0.1moll^{-1}
    (ii) Repeated to allow averages/mean to be calculated

  (b) (i) From right to left → arrow should be on wires or very close to it
    (ii) (good) conductor of electricity
      Contains delocalised electrons

CHEMISTRY INTERMEDIATE 2
2011

SECTION A

1.	B	11.	C	21.	A
2.	D	12.	C	22.	B
3.	A	13.	B	23.	D
4.	D	14.	B	24.	A
5.	A	15.	A	25.	D
6.	A	16.	D	26.	D
7.	D	17.	C	27.	B
8.	C	18.	D	28.	D
9.	A	19.	B	29.	C
10.	C	20.	C	30.	C

SECTION B

1. (a) 1st – covalent network
   2nd – ionic lattice
   3rd – metallic lattice
   4th – discrete covalent/covalent molecules

   (b) SiO_2
   O_2Si

2. (a)
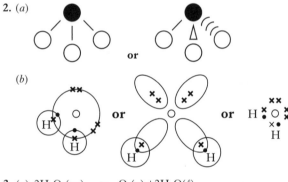

   (b)

3. (a) $2H_2O_2(aq) \longrightarrow O_2(g) + 2H_2O(\ell)$

   (b) to a syringe/
   downward displacement of water into a test-tube or measuring cylinder. Arrangement must work, eg no sealed delivery tubes

   (c) relights a glowing splint

   (d) 34g $\longrightarrow$ 12l
   1.7g $\longrightarrow$ 1.7/34 × 12
   = 0.6

   or
   No moles = 1.7/34 = 0.05
   Vol = 0.05 x 12
   = 0.6

   or
   34/1.7 = 20, then 12/20
   = 0.6

4. (a) (i) (catalyst) in same state/form/physical state as reactants

   (ii) $RuC\ell_2$ **or** $Ru^{2+}(C\ell^-)_2$ **or** **or** $Ru_1C\ell_2$

(b) (i)(ii)
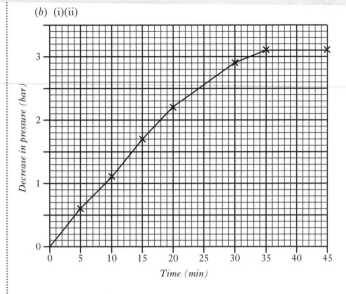

Time (min)

   (iii) $\dfrac{2\cdot2 - 1\cdot2}{10}$
   = 0.1

5. (a) Precipitation

   (b) 1 mole $(NH_4)_2SO_4$ = 132g

   Moles of $(NH_4)_2SO_4$ = $\dfrac{13200}{132}$ = 100 moles

   Moles of $(NH_4)_2CO_3$ = 100

   Moles of $(NH_4)_2CO_3$ = 100 × 96
   = 9600g/9.6Kg

   or

$(NH_4)_2CO_3$	$(NH_4)_2SO_4$
1 mole	1 mole
96 g	132 g
$\dfrac{13200}{132}$ × 96	13200g

   = 9600g/9.6kg

6. (a) To neutralise the acid, cancel out the acid, use up all/excess acid
   Move pH to 7

   (b)

   water —
   — $10cm^3$ starch solution
   +
   $1cm^3$ water

7. 1. crude oil
   2. styrene
   3. poly(ethenol)/polyethenol

8. (a) Presence of carbon monoxide/
   CO present/
   5% CO present

   (b) any value less than 3%

   (c) causes acid rain
   Sulphur dioxide reacts and produces/causes acid rain

9. (a) Photosynthesis

   (b) Enzyme/
   Biological catalyst

   (c) $CH_3 — CH_2 — OH/CH_3 ——CH_2OH$
   $CH_3\ CH_2\ OH/CH_3CH_2 —— OH$
   $CH_3\ CH_2(OH)$

(d) $\dfrac{9 \times 1.25}{3.8}$

$= 2.96$

10. (a) (i)

$$\begin{array}{ccc} H & & COOH \\ | & & | \\ C & = & C \\ | & & | \\ H & & H \end{array}$$

   (ii) Polar covalent

   (b) It partially ionises/
   It partially dissociates
   Doesn't dissociate easily
   Doesn't fully dissociate

11. (a) amine/
   amino

   (b) octyl ethanoate

   (c) (i) colourless to orange/brown/red/yellow

   (ii) 16.0

   (iii) moles of $Br_2 = 0.5 \times 0.016$
   $\qquad\qquad\quad = 0.008$

   moles of $C_{10}H_{16} = \dfrac{0.008}{2} = 0.004$

   concentration of $C_{10}H_{16} = \dfrac{0.004}{0.02}$
   $\qquad\qquad\qquad\qquad\qquad = 0.2$

12. (a) reduction

   (b) (i)
   $$\begin{array}{ccc} \text{Positive} & & \text{negative} \\ + & & - \end{array}$$
   (both required for 1 mark)

   (ii) Decolourise/bleaching of pH/litmus paper

13. (a) C

   (b) any value above 4.4 and below 6.0

14. (a) 3

   (b) 2 and 3

   (c) 0

   (d) it is covalent/glucose is covalent/contains no ions/not ionic

15. (a) (pH) will rise towards 7/
   (pH) will rise/
   (pH) becomes less acidic/
   increases/
   becomes neutral

   (b) $Ca_{10}(PO_4)_6F_2$

CHEMISTRY INTERMEDIATE 2 2012

SECTION A

1.	A	11.	B	21.	B
2.	B	12.	A	22.	B
3.	A	13.	D	23.	A
4.	D	14.	C	24.	C
5.	C	15.	A	25.	D
6.	D	16.	D	26.	B
7.	A	17.	C	27.	C
8.	A	18.	D	28.	D
9.	B	19.	C	29.	C
10.	A	20.	C	30.	D

SECTION B

1. (a) Network or Lattice

   (b) Sb_2O_3
   $(Sb^{3+})_2(O^{2-})_3$

   (c) (i) 11
   $\quad$ B
   $\quad$ 5

   (ii) Isotopes

2. (a) (i) $\dfrac{32 - 10}{8}$

   $\qquad = 2.75$

   (ii) 4.5

   (b) $NaN_3 \longrightarrow Na + N_2$

   (c) Explosive/
   Highly reactive/very reactive
   or
   Flammable
   or
   So that the nitrogen gas does not react with the sodium metal

3. (a)

Volume of water (cm^3)
0
2
4
6

   (b) Time taken until colour change/blue-black colour appears/
   Rate = 1/time **or** R =1/t
   or
   How quickly it turns blue/black

   (c) White tile/background under beaker to see colour change
   or
   Sharp/sudden/quick colour change

4. (a) Homogeneous

   (b) ½ mark for greater (surface) area
   ½ mark for <u>more</u> collisions/greater chance of collisions

   (c) $\dfrac{1.8}{90}$

   $\qquad = 0.02$

5. (a) ½ mark for same general formula
   ½ mark for similar/same (chemical) properties

   (b) (i) Greater number of carbon atoms, the greater the
   amount of heat (energy) (released)
   or

The larger/bigger the alkanal/molecule the more heat energy (released)

    (ii) 2800 to 3200

6. (a) (Very) strong/stronger than steel

    (b) (i)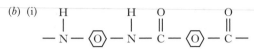

        (ii) Amide/peptide

7. (a) Hydration
      or
      Catalytic hydration

    (b) Ethyl propanoate

    (c)

$$H-\overset{\overset{\displaystyle H}{|}}{\underset{\underset{\displaystyle H}{|}}{C}}-\overset{\overset{\displaystyle H}{|}}{\underset{\underset{\displaystyle H}{|}}{C}}-\overset{\overset{\displaystyle H}{|}}{\underset{\underset{\displaystyle H}{|}}{C}}-\overset{\overset{\displaystyle H}{|}}{\underset{\underset{\displaystyle H}{|}}{C}}-OH$$

      or

$$H-\overset{\overset{\displaystyle H}{|}}{\underset{\underset{\displaystyle H}{|}}{C}}-\overset{\overset{\displaystyle H}{|}}{\underset{\underset{\displaystyle CH_3}{|}}{C}}-\overset{\overset{\displaystyle H}{|}}{\underset{\underset{\displaystyle H}{|}}{C}}-OH$$

      or

$$H-\overset{\overset{\displaystyle H}{|}}{\underset{\underset{\displaystyle H}{|}}{C}}-\overset{\overset{\displaystyle OH}{|}}{\underset{\underset{\displaystyle CH_3}{|}}{C}}-\overset{\overset{\displaystyle H}{|}}{\underset{\underset{\displaystyle H}{|}}{C}}-H$$

8. (a)

Observation with bromine solution	Saturated or unsaturated
No change	**Saturated**
Bromine decolourises	Unsaturated
No change	Saturated
Bromine decolourises	**Unsaturated**

    (b) Use a fume cupboard/well ventilated area
       Don't breathe in (bromine) fumes/
       Wear gloves
       Thiosulphate pesent

    (c) Cyclohexane or isomers of it

9. (a) ½ mark for add iodine (to water/sample/beaker)
       ½ mark for stays brown/red/orange/yellow
      or
      Turns blue/black if starch is present

    (b) (i) Glucose
          or
         Maltose

      (ii) Acid/
         Named Acid

10. (a) Trap sunlight/light
       or
      Harness energy from sun/
      Absorbs sunlight/
      Stores sun energy

    (b) Provides energy/
       Gives us energy

    (c) Lowers it/
       Decreases pH/
      Move it towards 7/ neutralises it

or
Goes down/
Makes it acidic

11. (a) A workable diagram:
       – Syringe (must have plunger)
      or Displacement of water into a vertical measuring cylinder/graduated test tube
      Diagram must not have closed-off tubes

    (b) Calcium chloride

    (c)

Volume of gas (cm³) vs *Time (min)* graph, y-axis 0 to 120, x-axis 0 to 10.

    ½ mark for correct labels and units
    ½ mark for scale on X and Y axis
    ½ mark for correct plotting of points
    ½ mark for joining of points (by ruler allowed)

12. (a) Hydrogen/H_2

    (b) One which does not completely ionise/dissociate
       One which partially ionise/dissociate (into ions)
      or
      Does not fully ionise
      or
      Partially breaks up/splits up
      or
      Partially ionises
      or
      Exists mainly as molecules

    (c) Circle lower   ½
       Circle higher   ½

13. (a) Precipitation

    (b) (i) $Ba^{2+}_{(aq)} + SO_4^{2-}_{(aq)} \longrightarrow Ba^{2+}SO_4^{2-}_{(s)}$
      (ii) Spectator (ions)

14. (a) Loses electron(s)
       Oxidises/oxidation
       Change into ions
       Forms a compound

    (b) (i) $Ag \longrightarrow Ag^+ + e$

      (ii) Positive (silver) ions are attracted to (negative) spoon/
        Silver ions are positive
        or
        So cutlery has constant supply of electrons for reduction of silver ions to take place on cutlery

15. (a) (i) $2 \times 0.25 = 0.5$

(ii) GFM $Fe_2O_3 = 160$

Moles of $Fe_2O_3 = \dfrac{0.5}{2} = 0.25$

or mole ratio stated

$Fe_2O_3 : H_3PO_4$
$1 : 2$

Mass of $Fe_2O_3 = 0.25 \times 160$
$= 40$

(b) Stops oxygen/air
or
Stops water/
or
Stops oxygen/air and water

CHEMISTRY INTERMEDIATE 2
2013

SECTION A

1.	B	11.	C	21.	C
2.	A	12.	C	22.	A
3.	B	13.	B	23.	D
4.	B	14.	C	24.	A
5.	C	15.	B	25.	D
6.	A	16.	B	26.	D
7.	B	17.	D	27.	A
8.	A	18.	C	28.	A
9.	D	19.	D	29.	B
10.	C	20.	A	30.	D

SECTION B

1. (a) (i) Red

(ii) Same group/
Same number of outer electrons/
Both in group 2/
Both alkaline earth metals

(b) LH electrode = positive/+
RH electrode = negative/–

2. (a) **Time** until cross can no longer be seen/
Rate = 1/time

(b) Concentration of sodium thiosulphate/
Volume of sodium thiosulphate/
Concentration of hydrochloric acid/
Volume of hydrochloric acid/
Size of beaker

(c) Carried out in a fume cupboard/
Don't breath in fumes/
Take care with sulphur dioxide given off

(d) Na^+/
Cl^-

3. (a) Hydrogen/
H_2/
H

(b) $\dfrac{72 - 0}{40} = 1.8$

(c) 0

(d) Slower/
Decreases/
Take longer to react

4. (a) Proton = 1
Neutron = 2
Electron = 1

(b) Protium

5. (a) Polar covalent/
Ionic

(b) (i) Increases and drops/decreases to zero
increases then decreases

(ii) Greater than 0.7 but less than 1.2 (not inclusive)

6. (a) $\dfrac{1.57}{157} = 0.01$ moles

(b) (Covalent)Network/
Lattice

(c) $Ca_3(PO_4)_2$
$(Ca^{2+})_3(PO_4^{3-})_2$
$(Ca^{2+})_3(PO_4)_2$
$Ca_3(PO_4^{3-})_2$

7. (a) carbon dioxide/
CO_2

(b) (i) $\dfrac{100 \times 70 \cdot 4}{56 \cdot 3} = 125 \cdot 04$

(ii) £130

8. (a) (Different) boiling points

(b) Increasing number of carbon atoms will increase viscosity(thickness)/
Decreasing carbon atoms will decrease viscosity(thickness)/
More carbons, greater viscosity(thickness)

(c) 2,3-dimethylbutane/
2,3 dimethylbutane/
2-3 dimethylbutane/
23- dimethylbutane

9. (a)

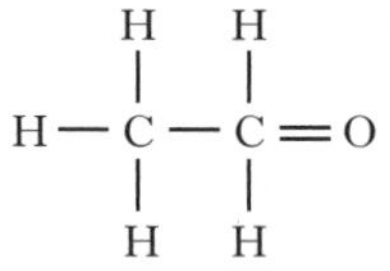

and

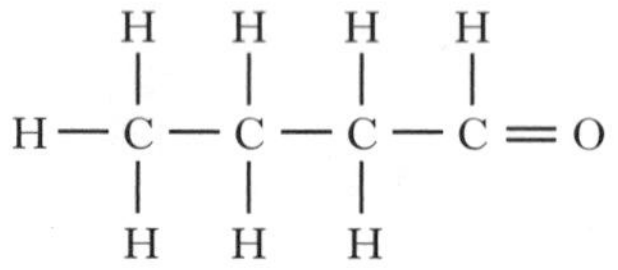

(b) (i) Butanoic acid

(ii) Turns lime water milky/chalky/cloudy

10. (a) Thermoplastic

(b) (i)

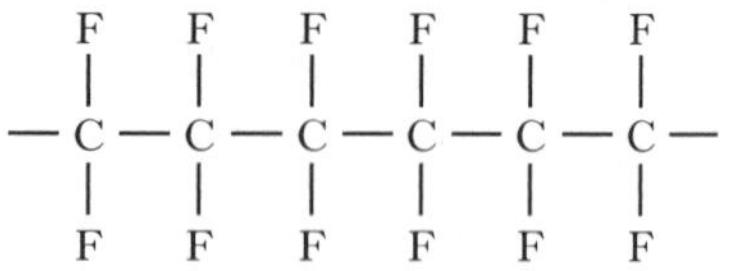

(ii) Addition

(c) Carbon monoxide/
CO

11. (a) 2,8,8

(b) (i)

(b) (ii)

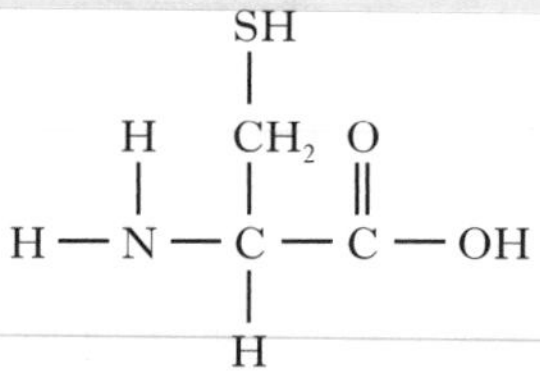

or

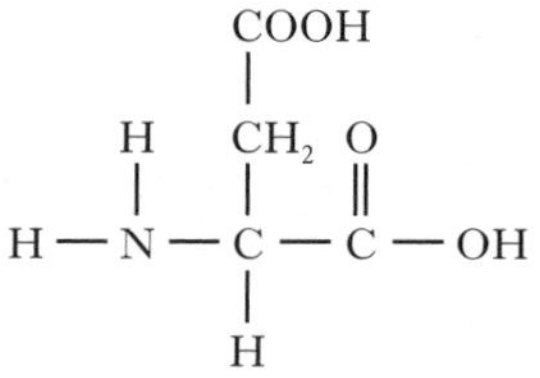

or

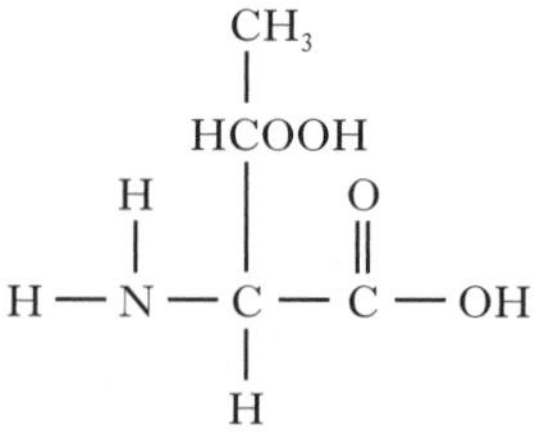

12. (a)

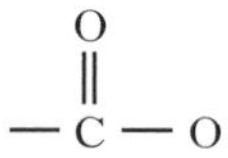

or

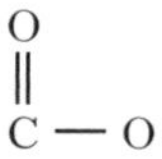

or

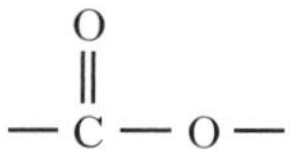

or

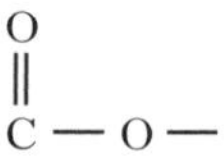

(b) Hydrolysis

(c) $\dfrac{8 \cdot 9}{890} \times 0 \cdot 01$ mole

$0 \cdot 01 \times 3 = 0 \cdot 03$ moles
GFM stearic acid = 284
Mass of stearic acid = $0 \cdot 03 \times 284 = 8 \cdot 52$

13. (a) (i) Any value less than 7

(ii)

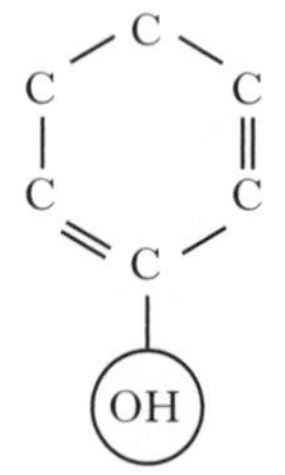

not

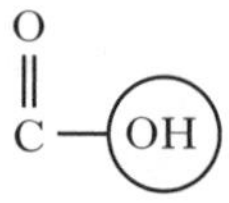

(b)

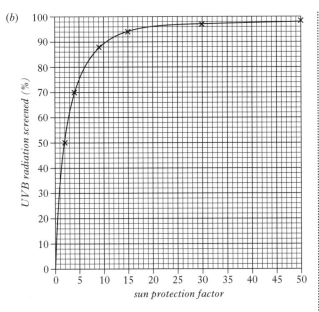

14. (a) To place zinc, magnesium and copper(metals) in order of reactivity
    Order of reactivity of metals

(b) To supply oxygen/O/O_2

(c) Magnesium –   very fast reaction/ fast/ fastest
                  Bursts into flames/
                  Burns with a bright white light

    Copper –   dull glow/
                  no reaction
                  Slow/ slowest
                  Moderately slow

(d) Potassium will explode/
    Potassium is too reactive/
    Boiling tube will explode/
    Test tube will break
    Reacts too vigorously/

15. (a) Less reactive/
    Lower down in ECS/
    Sodium is more reactive/
    Not as reactive as sodium/

(b) Na $\longrightarrow$ Na$^+$ + e

(c) Unreactive